full tilt

rebekah tyler

Dear Haurko

♡ Rebekah

x

Author's note: Some of the names, locations and details of events in this book have been changed to protect the privacy of persons involved.

First published in 2013 by Full Tilt Press

Cover artwork by Nina Rycroft

Produced by Mary Egan Publishing
www.maryegan.co.nz

Printed in USA by Shapco

ISBN 978-0-473-24742-3
eBook ISBN 978-0-473-24741-6

www.rebekahtyler.com
fulltiltpress@gmail.com
www.facebook.com/rebekah.tyler.165

For Nanny

Scene 1: Onboard a flight from Paris to Benin, West Africa
There was not a second to lose. As the carpet of Africa rolled out
beneath us, I squeezed into the airplane toilet determined to undergo
a metamorphosis. My comfy pink velour tracksuit was hurriedly dis-
carded for something much more alluring. Heads turned and African
men made kissing sounds as I returned to my seat. I have to admit it:
I've got a talent. Give me fifteen minutes anywhere and voila – I'm
a sex kitten!

On arrival I stepped precariously down the steep metal staircase
into the sizzling heat rising from the tarmac. I was wearing black stilettos, a skin-tight leopard-print dress and a full face of makeup; who
cared if it didn't last in the furious African heat? I had come to Benin
for a six-week holiday with Stephan, a French-Canadian geologist
with whom I had shared a twenty-minute in-flight conversation a few
weeks earlier. Not even Africa's hot, dusty landscape could deter me
from looking like the woman of Stephan's dreams.

It worked. Twelve weeks later, with numb toes, I stood shivering
in the Montreal snow wearing a strapless wedding dress and golden
heels, anxiously waiting to say 'I do.'

Five months later Marco was born.

Four years after that my lawyer called.

'Your divorce is final.'

Scene 2: Montreal Airport Customs hall

As an exhausted and disheveled New Zealand mother, I arrived back at Montreal Airport, accompanied by ten-year-old Marco and two-year-old Jack, both insomniac and excited.

- Number of hours confined within planes: 18
- Number of toys thrown by Jack during flight: 28
- Number of wines consumed in my state of fatigue: 7
- Number of sympathetic fellow passengers on flight: zero.

Chance of changing into a sex kitten during this flight? Are you kidding? The only thing I was changing was a nappy!

I waited to claim our baggage, feeling shocked as reality dawned: was I really about to spend eight months travelling the world with my two young boys?

It was only yesterday that my dear friend Lucy had offered to meet me at Auckland Airport with Marco and Jack. She'd spent the day looking after them while I packed up our entire life. I had spent the morning lugging boxes and furniture into a storage unit and the afternoon packing suitcases. It had been a long time since I'd had a day to myself. Perhaps that explained the state of calmness I felt sitting alone in the taxi on the way to the airport. I was able to breathe.

Without the constant demands of two young boys, I had the chance to notice music playing on the driver's radio. I wasn't a fan of country, but anything sounded great without the distraction of two boys quibbling. I looked down at my mother's gold ring engraved with moons and stars glistening on my right hand. I pulled out a small bottle from my handbag and sprayed a little of my grandmother's remaining Chanel No 5 on my neck, daydreaming that I was off on an exotic adventure by myself.

The taxi came to a halt and two boys banged hard on my window.

'Mummy, Mummy! Hurry the plane's leaving.'

'Just relax, boys. We have plenty of time.'

'Let's go! Come on! Come on Mum!' Marco cried, choosing to ignore my previous comment as he dragged me towards the check-in counter. Jack giggled and jumped as he tried to grab the tickets for the immigration officer. If there was one thing I didn't have to worry about it was the boys' eagerness to see the world.

I felt happy to see Marco and Jack so excited, but five minutes after we waved goodbye to Lucy, my happiness turned to anxiety as I restrained Jack from shoving the luggage trolley into the ankles of a tall man waiting to check in for our flight. He patted Jack on the head and grinned, excusing the toddler's behaviour. I was certain that his crooked smile in my direction was definitely one of pity.

For eighteen hours with little respite, Jack threw plastic cutlery and metal Hot Wheel cars into the laps of furious passengers who were, luckily, many rows in front. He squealed as he terrorised the people around us. As they turned and glared, searching for the mother responsible, I did my best to shrink into my seat. I envied Marco's oblivion – thanks to earplugs and a Nintendo.

I thought that because the boys seemed so excited to travel, maybe it wouldn't be as hard as people warned. If the first eighteen hours of our family's liberation confirmed anything, it was that life for the next eight months was not going to be stress-free.

During the second leg of our trip, from Los Angeles to Montreal, the three of us were sitting between two buyers from Guess clothing. Jack, being the friendly child that he was, kept stroking their shoes and offering to feed them remnants of his half-eaten beef casserole. The young man seemed taken by Jack's open nature. However, his middle-aged female companion (who obviously didn't have children of her own) scowled as though Jack had some life-threatening disease. When Jack made a move near her, she flinched in a bid to ward him off.

I was extremely tempted to wipe his sticky chocolate fingers all over her red silk trouser suit.

Six hours later I watched Marco wrestle his screaming brother off the conveyer belt as I waited for our suitcases to arrive. Had I really abandoned the security of my safe suburban life to embark on a journey around the world? Had I actually sold my house of seventeen years to pay for this trip? Had I really quit my new teaching job after spending five years studying at university? Perhaps I should have listened to my friends who came over before we left. They had wanted to confirm I was really going ahead with my plans. Horror streaked across their faces as they said goodbye. One by one they repeated, 'You must be mad!'

Was I?

I guess there was only one way to find out.

PART 1
Life Before

Chapter 1

I was once taken to a rubbish dump for a date. Although I was only thirteen and desperately searching for love, I do wish I had set my expectations a bit higher from the start.

Even in my twenties I kept looking for love in all the wrong places and my romantic encounters never ended well: I was the victim of infidelity, the target for a hunting knife and threatened with a bow and arrow. On one occasion, I was abducted by an English beau who was later deported. Oh, the wretchedness I endured when I was young and in love, or at least, wishing I was.

By twenty-eight, I concluded I was never going to find happiness in love. That was before I met Stephan.

Stephan and I met the day after my twenty-ninth birthday while I was working as a flight attendant for Air New Zealand. I had been stealing a nap while the plane sat on the tarmac at Sydney Airport. I was desperate for some rest after a four a.m. start and only two hours sleep the night before, as I had been crying in bed until two a.m. waiting for my current boyfriend to arrive to wish me happy birthday.

He never came.

After three hours sleep in the crew bunks, I awoke with a start to the sound of passengers boarding. I rushed to take my place in the aisle, too tired to worry about fixing my smudged makeup and messy French plait, too worn-out to smile at the passengers looking for their seats, until I spotted a good-looking man walking down the far aisle of the plane. I noticed his dark smouldering eyes, chiselled cheekbones, toffee-coloured skin, French-Canadian accent – enough to decide I should go and fix my makeup and hair after all.

He must have hardly recognised me when I returned transformed and asking if he desired, 'Coffee, tea or me?'

The effort obviously paid off. After exchanging addresses and then writing to each other for several months, he invited me to visit him in Africa where he was working as a geologist. I dumped my fickle boyfriend and jumped on a plane. A few weeks later, Stephan proposed in Paris. Not long afterwards, he asked me to accompany him home to Montreal to meet his family. His mother, Simone, embraced me as we met. Two weeks later, I walked down the aisle and married her son. Marco was born five months later.

Unfortunately when I was thirty-three, Stephan and I divorced, leaving me to raise our two-year-old son alone.

Jack's story began with a bad date. The guy's name was David and I had met him while camping with Marco in New Zealand's Coromandel. Having just completed five years of study for a Bachelor of Arts and a Diploma of Teaching – I promised Marco we would spend some quality time together. Coromandel's Miranda Hot Springs sounded like the perfect place with its thermal mineral pools inside a small campground.

David and I connected instantly in the campsite's communal kitchen during a dishwashing session. Just as things were heating up between us, Marco came running into the kitchen.

'Please, please, please can we go to the pool now? It closes in ten minutes,' Marco begged.

When David caught me looking alternately at Marco's pleading eyes and my large pile of dirty dishes he said, 'If you want to go, I'll keep an eye on your things.'

When I returned from our swim half-an-hour later, David was gone and my dirty dishes were sparkling clean and piled neatly.

The next morning, David cycled off back to Auckland, but not before finding me to bid me farewell. Unfortunately for him, he made the mistake of gazing into my eyes just a bit too long.

Unable to stop thinking about David's eyes (not to mention his mastery at cleaning dishes) for several days, I decided to find the object of my campsite desire. I did what any woman would do and bought a copy of the Auckland Electoral Roll, which had a list of all registered voters' first names, surnames, addresses and professions. He struck me as the kind of man who would be civically responsible enough to vote.

Then began the arduous task of locating David. All I knew about him was his first name and that he was a school teacher in Auckland. Praying there wouldn't be too many Davids who fitted the same bill, I began combing through the Electoral Roll's 40,000 listings, alphabetically ordered by surname. Unbelievably, 35,000 names later, I found his name on page 176, under the letter S. I searched for his name in the telephone book and dialed his home number. As the phone rang it dawned on me that in some places in the world, men might think I was a stalker rather than a persistent and love-searching woman.

So you're probably thinking that David is Jack's father. I would have liked that to be the case but he didn't end up sticking around long enough.

We did have a brief affair, which included him visiting for home-cooked dinners and reading bedtime stories to Marco. A few weeks after our first date we met for lunch in a city café. I hoped he'd invite me back to his place and to ensure nothing got in the way, I even placed Marco in childcare for the afternoon. Perhaps after opening a bottle of Moët, David would play Leonard Cohen's *Dance Me to the End of Love* and we would spend the next four hours swaying in a tight embrace and kissing the afternoon away.

When the offer did not come, I invited myself.

I wasn't prepared for his decline; especially so calmly, so non-committedly, so unapologetically.

I stormed out of the café, leaving my uneaten salmon and cream cheese bagel (and it was really good salmon), jumped into my car and sped off towards the Auckland Harbour Bridge with Pat Benatar's *Love is a Battlefield* blaring. Not only had my heart been broken once again, I was also wearing my red satin date-dress. With my afternoon of freedom, I had nowhere to go. I turned up the stereo, let the wind blow through my hair and decided to find another man to love.

Of course to have energy for that, I needed some lunch first, so I headed to my local supermarket to pick up some wine and chocolate. When I parked the car and stepped out, there he was: Jack's dad.

Our eyes locked instantly as he drove past me looking for a park. He smiled. I smiled back. He had a twinkle in his eye. He circled me again (the shark imagery should have been a warning) and parked his car. A friend saw me and came over to chat. Bloody hell, whatever it was, could she just hurry up? She was restricting my view. I managed to lean back far enough to offer him one last smile as he left his car and walked in the opposite direction. Too hungry to pursue this handsome man right now (I really needed some chocolate), but determined not to let him slip through my fingers, I took down his car's registration plate and placed it safely in my pocket. Then I bought myself a bottle of Moët and a king-size bar of Cadbury's Fruit and Nut – and dug right in.

On my way home, I drove to the post office and handed over his car's registration details, along with two dollars. It was scary how easy it was to obtain the owner's name and address. With this vital information, I was able to look him up in the phone book. I rang immediately and left a message. He called back a few hours later.

That was June.

By July I was pregnant.

By August Jack's dad had done a runner.

A day in the life of this single mum:

A.M.:

6.00 Change Jack's wet bed sheets.

6.05 Shower and dress Jack.

6.15 Make hot chocolate for Jack.

6.20 Boil jug for coffee. Open jar. Empty.

6.30 Wake up Marco.

6.45 Feed 2 x hungry boys pancakes with maple syrup.

6.50 Clean maple syrup spillage on carpet.

7.00 Make 2 x lunchboxes (drink, sandwich, apple and 2 chocolate-chip cookies). Stop boys pleading for more cookies.

7.05 Hurriedly kiss Marco goodbye before he leaves for school.

7.10 Dress myself in my hole-ridden pink velour tracksuit.

7.15 Look in the mirror. Notice the dark bags under my eyes. Wait! Are those new wrinkles?

7.20 Spend ten minutes looking for eyeliner. Find it buried under a pile of crayons. Look at the clock. Out of time for makeup.

7.25 Feel guilty for forgetting to wave goodbye to Marco through the kitchen window as too busy looking for eyeliner.

7.30 Put pee-soaked sheets in washing machine. Curse myself for not spending more time toilet-training Jack.

7.35 Go back to mirror. Notice the dark hair growing on my upper lip.

7.40 Load dishwasher.

7.45 Hang out load of washing.

7.50 Put second load of washing on.

8.00 Make beds and vacuum quickly.

8.10 Reading homework with Jack.

8.15	Walk Jack to school. Kiss him goodbye.
8.30	School crossing duty.
9.00	Parent-help in class for 2 hours.
11.00	Walk home.
11.15	Realise have not had breakfast. Eat while emptying dishwasher.
11.20	Ring beautician to book an upper lip wax appointment.

P.M.:

12.00	Write manuscript for ten minutes.
12.30	Teach at the local kindergarten for the afternoon.
3.00	Pick up Jack.
3.15	Drive 30 minutes for Jack's gymnastics, eating lunch on the way.
4.45	Drive from gym to pick up Marco from Robotics.
5.00	Buy groceries.
5.30	Cook dinner.
6.00	Eat dinner and prepare lessons for tomorrow's part-time teaching job.
6.15	Bring in washing. Fold.
6.25	Lay towel and hot wax on floor ready to wax legs. Answer phone. Return to find wax spilled all over the carpet.
6.30	Showers x 3.
6.45	Load dishwasher.
7.00	Read bedtime story to Jack (skip two chapters).
7.15	Drink a large glass of chardonnay.
7.20	Yell, 'Goodnight!' to Marco.
7.30	Lie comatosed on couch watching *The Bachelor*.
9.00	Wake and drag myself to bed.
9.30	Dream I'm drinking cocktails on a tropical island.

Next day – do it all over again!

Shortly after Jack turned one I planned to celebrate my fortieth birthday. Two weeks before this celebration my grandmother, Nanny, died suddenly and my '60s-themed fancy dress party was replaced by her wake.

The night before the wake, Nanny looked very serene as she lay in her coffin in my living room with a pink geranium behind her ear. Her skin was luminous and free of lines, and her torso poised and erect – no longer the pale, wrinkled, skeletal frame stooped under the burden of its own weight. I sat on the carpet next to her, sorting through the photos of her life.

Nanny had spent the last few weeks before her death in a rest home, recuperating after a fall that had left her with three broken ribs. I tried to convince her that was the best place for her to recover, but she hated being there.

'It's full of old people mumbling, smelling of urine, pushing their false teeth in and out and coughing,' she had told me the day after she moved in. One week later, I met one of these 'old people' – his name was Fred.

Though Fred hardly talked, he laughed a lot. Nanny couldn't stand his laughter. She appreciated a good sense of humour, as much as the next person, but not Fred's. She hated the way he laughed at everything, all the time. The only thing Nanny found worse than his laughter was his pajama bottoms. They constantly fell down due to the worn elastic around his waist. On one particular occasion when Fred was walking down the narrow corridor to the dining room with my Nanny tailing close behind (both with the assistance of their Zimmer frames) Fred must have stopped ten times or more in order to hitch up his pants. Nanny, who was ordinarily quite patient, could not tolerate this stop-start procedure and finally yelled, 'For God's sake, get a move on!' He responded the only way an eighty-four-year-old laughing man could, 'Fuck off!'

Nanny begged me to bring her 'home' to my house, where she had lived for the previous ten years.

'I don't want to die here,' she said to me every day when I talked to her. Those words still haunt me to this day, because, despite my promises to the contrary, she did.

I had promised Nanny I would bring her home. It might have been too late, but at least I had done it. So, as I watched my boys standing beside her coffin posing for photographs, mild relief washed over me. I had managed in some small way to grant Nanny her last wish.

Later that evening, the warm oil heater and small bedside light placed next to Nanny's coffin made the room feel cosy. Cliff Richard played on the stereo and four sherry glasses were lined in a row awaiting the arrival of my three cousins.

They never came. No one did.

Two hours later, my brief feeling of calm gave way to a flood of grief. I found only enough energy to call my friend Lucy who dropped everything to drive over and hug me. We sat crumpled on the floor at the foot of Nan's coffin for hours, sipping glass after glass of Nan's much-loved tipple.

Standing over Nanny's motionless body in her coffin reminded me of the time when I was about three years old, standing beside my mother while she was on the phone. I had tugged at her skirt, wanting her to finish her conversation and continue to make Christmas decorations with me. When I saw her collapse I took the receiver and told her friend on the end of the line that, 'Mummy has gone to sleep.' Then I heard the ambulance siren scream.

One year later my mother would be dead.

She was twenty-four years old.

My mother had been in and out of hospital with a heart condition from the time I was born. Nanny had always been there to look after me during her absence. For four years, Nanny took me on the bus for daily visits to see my mother. I have only fond memories of those outings to the hospital. I remember sitting in her ward for hours, brushing the hair of the elderly patients who loved the little girl who visited her mother every day. When, at four, I was orphaned after my mother died from a heart attack, Nanny raised me without question.

It took Nanny weeks after my mother's funeral to tell me that, 'Mummy is dead and she won't be coming back.' She had to deal with her own grief first.

I had been giving my big doll a bath when Nanny called me into the kitchen and sat me down at the yellow Formica table. As soon as Nanny told me I cried and cried. Nanny pulled me close to her, wiped my eyes with her handkerchief and offered me a bag of red and yellow pear drops so my tears ceased. I wonder whether Jack or Marco would react in the same way if I died. Would they be as resilient? Would they too find refuge in a bag of sweets? Or had I no real attachment to my mother because she had been ill from my birth? Maybe Nanny had already become my whole world?

Initially, Nanny and I lived in a little flat over a sweet shop on North London's bustling High Street. Being squeezed into a row of identical flats made ours a dark home. To console me, Nanny let me sneak under her purple candlewick bedspread, delighting in the car lights from the traffic below that circled our room.

What fascinated me must have tormented Nanny. She had lost her two-storied brick home in the leafy London suburb of Totteridge a few years before, when her husband of twenty-odd years left her for a woman thirty years his junior. My mother's cousin Sarah said that Nanny had been proud of their terraced house and garden. She had personally constructed several narrow stone paths between flowerbeds of red and yellow roses. What wonderful opportunities that space afforded my mother, her cousins and Judy the dog to play and dream. Sarah also recalled the solace of the kitchen that regularly exuded the sweet aroma of creamy milk jelly made with evaporated milk. What a loss Nanny must have felt the day she moved out.

After Nanny's funeral I found an old black-and-white photograph tucked into a small side pocket in her purse. In it, Nanny is having afternoon tea with her sister Marjorie and two nieces at her family home before her marriage fell apart. I can picture her, beaming proudly on her terrace, pouring tea into hand-painted china cups from her silver teapot.

Even years later Nanny continued to hold her head high and keep smiling. I might never have guessed her on-going heartbreak had I not glimpsed her wiping her eyes looking out our flat's sullied windows as she polished the small bundle of silver she had salvaged from her marriage.

Despite losing my mum at four, Nanny made sure my childhood was filled with joy and laughter. Looking back, I marvel how she did it. She did not provide material wealth and we never owned a house or a car. What she offered was something much more valuable: the desire to make the most of every day of my life.

This lesson Nanny taught me best through her decision in 1976, when she was in her late sixties, to emigrate with me to New Zealand. She hoped it would bring a better life for both of us. Though she didn't have many possessions to sell or abandon, she did leave behind her two elderly sisters and brother, whom she adored. Even thirty years later, Nanny's longing for her family in England was something she never truly stopped yearning for.

It was my Uncle Andrew, who'd moved to New Zealand a few months earlier, who persuaded Nanny to leave London. He assured her it would be a better place to raise me. Nonetheless, I think she was ready for her next adventure.

Less rational at nine years old, it took Uncle Andrew's promise of a pony for me to agree to leave England and, let me just say, I never did get a pony. Years later I found a coaster with a picture of an angelic-looking girl asking innocently enough, 'Where's my fucking pony?' I mailed it to my Uncle Andrew for Christmas.

I'm still waiting.

Being a hard-working, self-reliant woman meant that Nanny had to work well into her seventies as an accounts clerk to afford the costs of raising me. She would leave the house at seven each morning and travel by ferry and bus to her office, and she often worked late into the night after she returned. It was hard enough for her to keep up with basic living costs. Nanny couldn't afford to buy my school uniform, so I had to sew my own. I felt ugly in my skirt that was different from the other girls' uniforms. We never had the money for luxury items like a telephone. Can you imagine being a teenage girl without this vital piece of technology? I hated being the only one in my class unable to chat to girlfriends after school.

Even in her eighties, Nanny practised extreme thriftiness. On the occasional visit to a restaurant, she made sure she had a piece of tinfoil in her bag. That way she could pilfer a little something from the buffet to take home. This penny-pinching sometimes backfired, resulting in gravy leaking from the foil all over her handbag.

Instead of becoming bitter about her role as breadwinner, Nanny embraced this opportunity to surround herself with young and vibrant colleagues. Never one to sit at home alone or bored, she would jump at the chance for a night out with coworkers or a joyride. Once a colleague took her for a spin in his vintage Mercedes convertible. While driving, he stopped abruptly causing Nanny to bang her head on the windscreen. Nor did she miss an opportunity for practical jokes, arriving at work next day with a bandage wrapped around her head and a large orange tucked inside. She sure gave that driver the scare of his life.

Working with a younger generation also gave Nanny the opportunity to stay trendy. She would swap clothes with the young women she worked with and at lunchtime they would go to a local salon for a cut and dye. No, Nanny never let herself get old. That was why she refused to hang out with anyone her own age.

'They're old and lacklustre,' she'd say, as she sat down to her meal, forgetting to turn off the stove for the fourth time that week.

Nanny's desire to stay forever young moved her to take over the organisation of my sixteenth birthday party.

'I'm taking you and six friends to your first nightclub,' she told me. She was not deterred by the fact that the legal age of entry was eighteen. Nanny and my friends and I danced to the rock and roll music of Tom Sharplin and his band till the early hours of the morning. The thick clouds of cigarette smoke and the smell of dark rum were intoxicating and much more exciting than the 'sleepover' parties that most of my friends were having at the time. When we returned to my boyfriend's V8 car, we discovered the car park had been locked at midnight. Living across the harbour, our only choice was to take a taxi but Nanny only had twenty dollars left. The unsympathetic taxi driver drove until the money ran out and then made us get out and walk the rest of the way. It was cold and dark and my friends and I became scared. Nanny began to laugh and we joined in, linked arms and walked, but Nanny's smile soon disappeared when a father stood waiting for us at home for his daughter. It was pretty awkward, even for Nanny, telling him that his sixteen-year-old daughter had gone home with a sailor.

At times Nanny's work kept her away from home, which meant at the age of nine I would often have to cook my own dinner. Sometimes I envied my friends whose stay-at-home mothers would greet them at the door at the end of the school day with a plate of club sandwiches. Still, I did not miss out altogether. After all, Nanny's absence taught me that if I opened Delia Smith's *Frugal Food* cookbook, I could make my own.

Even at eighty-four, Nanny was fierce and determined. Like the time she came to my place for dinner and during the meal complained that her fork was heavier than usual. I assured her that it was the same fork she had been eating with for the last ten years and ignored her remark. After our meal we sat down on the couch to watch Princess Diana's funeral on the television. We were captivated by the elaborate ceremony, not speaking for some time watching thousands of grieving people lining the London streets. Suddenly I looked over at her and noticed the left side of her face drooping.

'Nanny, your face looks funny,' I said. 'Oh my God! Nanny! It's a stroke! Are you having a stroke? Come, put on your coat! I'll drive you to the hospital. Let's get to the hospital!'

I had already leapt up, terrified that Nanny was about to die.

'No, Rebekah. I want to wait. We'll go after the funeral is finished. I want to see the end.'

Her voice sounded firm. I grabbed the phone anyway and started to dial.

'Please don't call. Just wait,' she insisted.

With my coat on, I sat down again. Not until Diana was laid to rest would she let me call the ambulance. As far as my grandmother was concerned, strokes could wait.

Although Nanny lived until ninety-three years old, a long life by any standard, her death left me in shock. My boys aside, she had been my only close family. My mother, my father, my grandparents, my siblings – all rolled into one.

I was now alone in the world with two young boys dependent on me.

Although Marco cried when he picked up the book he and his great-grandmother had read at bedtime, he was still just a child who wanted his dinner. Like me, all those years ago when Nanny had told me about my mother's death, Marco and Jack did not fully understand the finality of death. Instead, the boys were all smiles as Marco repositioned the pink geranium behind Nanny's ear before posing for a photograph beside her.

The funeral was followed by days of continuous sobbing and an inability to eat or get out of my pajamas. Marco begged me to stop. He needed his mother to cook dinner, to clean the house, to be cheery once again. It was the first time I fully realised that he and Jack were depending on me the way I had been depending on Nanny. I knew that I had to find some way of moving on.

So I sold my house, quit my job and rang a travel agent.

PART 2

Canada

Chapter 2

Staggering through Montreal Airport's Customs hall laden with ten pieces of baggage (children included), I collapsed into the arms of the Rodrigues family. Their warm smiles coupled with a box of fresh sugary donuts were a welcome relief after the many hours of travel.

Ten years earlier, I had arrived on their doorstep four months pregnant, to marry their son and brother Stephan.

My mother-in-law Simone's deep love for me and happiness for her son, made it impossible for both Stephan and me to tell her we were separating only two years later. We could not bear to see her disappointment and sadness, especially as she kept telling me she was so happy we had married. When she invited us to stay with her shortly after, Stephan and I shared a room for eight nights, just to keep up pretences. It was not easy lying side-by-side in a double bed, that felt like a single, when we were already finalising our divorce papers. I bought myself long red flannelette pajamas covered in a purple teddy bear print and each night buttoned them up to the neck and rolled over to the very edge of the bed.

A year later, Stephan and I finally found the courage to visit Simone and tell her we were divorced and that I was living in New Zealand and Stephan was living and working in Africa. She hugged me and cried.

Five years later, during a visit at Christmas, I trembled at the thought of telling Simone I was pregnant with Jack. Would she be disappointed? She was the matriarch of a large Catholic family and, being the sort of Catholic whose faith moved her to attend church twice a day, I had no idea how she would react to Jack being born out of wedlock. Would she love my new baby like she loved Marco, knowing Stephan wasn't the father? Forgetting the French word for 'pregnant' I lifted my blouse slightly to reveal my swollen belly. Simone stopped chopping onions and once again held me in her arms.

The Rodrigues' love and support for me had never wavered since I divorced Stephan, so I hoped that nothing was going to change when I introduced Jack to my ex-mother-in-law, Simone.

Two years later, we huddled together in the airport terminal at the beginning of our world trip and Simone held out her arms and embraced Jack.

'*Bonjour mon petit, Jack. Je suis Grandmaman,*' Simone said, holding him with the same deep affection she'd always bestowed on Marco. Luckily for me, Simone manifested her faith by doing all she could to make others feel loved and cared for. This is something she had learned as a child growing up in Quebec. Being the eldest of fifteen children, it was her duty to help raise her siblings. There was little time for playing with dolls, or riding bikes when there were daily loads of clothes to be laundered, seventeen plates of food to be cooked, and fourteen younger children to look after.

For her, we were blood relatives and that was that. I tried to hold back the tears, but it was impossible.

Another member of the family who showered Jack with love and kindness during our eight-week stay in Canada was Stephan's sister Danielle, or Dan, as we called her. When we stayed with Dan and her husband Francois, we hardly ever left her house. She was content to stay home; it was her most treasured possession and the place where she felt most comfortable. Pink walls, yellow curtains covered in daisies and sparkly crystal ornaments adorned the living room. The bathroom was decorated in pink tiles and lace curtains, and Dan and Francois' bedroom was draped in little blue and purple flowers, from bedspread to curtains.

Unlike me, Dan had never left her country. 'I don't want to travel. I have everything I need at home,' she told me when I begged her to visit me in New Zealand. The heart of her home was the kitchen. Food was constantly on Dan's mind. Her kitchen overflowed with recipe books, kitchen gadgets and a super-sized refrigerator bursting with gourmet foods. It was understood that she took great pride in what she placed on the table and expected only the highest praise. This is why the roof nearly blew off when her husband Francois complained about the sandwich she had made a few months after they had married.

'How am I supposed to eat this sandwich? It is so huge!'

Dan's fist slammed down on the three-tiered bread and filling, squashing it flat.

'There! Is it better?' she bellowed.

In the twenty years of marriage that followed Francois never complained again.

During our two-week visit Auntie Dan spent hours in the kitchen cooking with Jack. Back home I had often intended to do the same, but with the risk of eggs and flour coating the floor, I denied Jack the pleasure. It was easier and quicker to do it myself. Occasionally when I let the boys into the kitchen I relied on my old mate Betty (as in Crocker) to support me. That way it was over and done with in a few minutes, with minimal mess. You would never know I once worked as a London-trained professional chef at the five-star Grosvenor House Hotel in Park Lane. Now I'm an exhausted mother, who's traded panfrying fillet steaks with béarnaise sauce, scalloped potatoes and ratatouille for a can of baked beans on toast.

Most of the time at home it is just the three of us – Marco, Jack and myself. Although I believe I provide a loving and stable environment for my children I want them to grow up with fond memories of spending time with loving adults, friends and family other than myself. My longing for the boys to feel they were part of a bigger family was perhaps a result of my own childhood spent alone with Nanny. As a child I sat for hours in my bedroom cutting out images of babies, children and mothers from Mothercare mail order catalogues. I would then arrange them in families by writing first and last names on the back of each image. I would always group a mother with one child. To me, that was a family.

Because of this, I have fostered the boys' relationship with their Canadian family – people who cheered and clapped as Marco rode his bike with no training wheels for the first time, people who pinned up Jack's kindergarten photograph on their fridge with pride, and people who eagerly played hour-long card games and ate meals accompanied by the boisterous chatter of two boys. Consequently, seeing Jack laugh and run into Auntie Dan's arms after an hour of snowball fighting with Uncle Francois made me so happy.

It wasn't just the boys who benefited from staying with Dan and Francois. I also anticipated entering the kitchen each morning with Dan singing, 'Wake up, wake up, it's time to get up,' while she brewed fresh coffee and cooked homemade pancakes.

My bond with the Rodrigues family was strengthened by our mutual love of food, which served as the foundation of their home and family life. *Grandmaman*, Dan and I spent hours cooking traditional Quebec meat pies encased in salty, buttery pastry, preserving tomato and rhubarb ketchup and baking Angel cakes.

More pleasure came from weekly fondues, which were never devoured by fewer than twelve famished family members. We would shout and elbow each other as our skewers sparred in a battle for the tender beef that fell into the stock steaming in the fondue pot.

In the end our buttons popped and our zippers unzipped, but this did not stop us from savouring the dessert that followed: Danielle's Angel cake accompanied by Simone's fresh strawberry coulis. When every crumb had disappeared, cards and dice would replace the plates and a fierce game of Yahtzee or Skip Bo would commence. The abundance of such delicious food plus the addition of chips and chocolate to accompany the game was the reason I was at least three kilos heavier by the time I left for England.

Although I treasured our time with the Rodrigues', being a guest in somebody else's house with a two-year-old boy was not easy. I felt constantly on edge, aware of the damage a toddler could do suddenly without warning.

Fortunately, I didn't have this worry with Marco. He was always stretched out on the couch reading one of the ten books he borrowed each week from the local library, or else making clay figurines and filming them in the hope of working at Weta Workshop when he was older. Most boys he knew wanted to be policemen and astronauts; Marco wanted to make special effects for Peter Jackson's future films.

Visiting peoples' houses with Jack was a different story – he was difficult to contain. On one occasion, in New Zealand, Jack thought it would be a good idea to wander around the garden pulling out all of my friend's newly planted daisies. This situation might have been excused if he had not proceeded to make a magic potion with the daisies and a bucket of mud, which he spread over her brand new paving stones.

Jack also hated going to bed.

'No!' he'd shout, while I struggled to put his pajamas on.

'I want to play dice and watch Indiana Jones.'

This was made harder when Danielle and Francois played The Stampeders' rendition of *Hit the Road Jack* at full volume just before

Jack's bedtime. Dancing and singing would commence, pots and pans would be transformed into instruments and *Chez Dan* would rock.

When I finally gained control, he would then escape from his bed and bound exuberantly into the living room. So, I should have known something was astray when one night Jack went off to bed in silence. As I slowly turned the knob to check his bedroom he sprinted towards me with an air of satisfaction.

Then I saw it.

Jack-Jack from *The Incredibles* had struck. The white sheets on his bed were covered with the artwork of Jack Tyler. In black permanent marker.

I returned to the living room and pretended I'd seen nothing.

'Was Jack alright?' Dan asked.

'Perfect. An absolute angel.'

'Of course he is,' she said, beaming.

I was just about to ask where Dan bought the sheets when she stood up and pulled out a plastic bag.

'Look at this wonderful pirate ship I found on sale today at Toys"R"Us,' she said.

I tried to look enthusiastic as Dan showed me the gleaming red-and-black toy ship.

'Dan, I wanted to know …' I began.

'I can't wait to give it to Jack tomorrow,' Dan interrupted, 'a treat for helping me bake this morning. He is such a good boy.'

If only!

I waited for my chance to change the subject. Then it came. Dan put down the ship and reached for the remote control and I casually asked her where she had bought the sheets in Jack's room.

'They're so soft,' I added. 'They would be perfect for my new bed back home.' I was already planning which day I could go into town, buy new ones and discreetly replace them.

'Oh those. I'm so glad you like them. My elderly aunt handmade them years ago. She meant the world to me. And those are the only thing I have left to remind me of her.'

As a mother, knowing that Jack, like myself, would never feel the arms of a father's embrace made me extremely sad. A few days before leaving New Zealand for our travel, I picked Jack up from his daycare and noticed two dads arrive early to pick up their children. The two men sat either side of Jack on the mat as the teacher read to the children. My heart tightened as I watched Jack look lovingly left to right at these two men who had placed their own boys on their laps and wrapped their arms tightly around them.

I know some people might argue that my choices in life have caused Jack's fatherless situation. For years, it's been convenient to tell my friends and myself that my pregnancy was an accident. Until, one day recently, my straight-talking editor reprimanded me, saying, 'Unless a penis flew into your vagina, it was no accident.' Regardless, I don't think my cock-ups should act as the blueprint for my boys' future. Jack deserves to be loved as much as any child.

One Father's Day, Jack returned from daycare and reached into his little blue backpack.

'Look Mummy,' he said, pulling a bright orange card from his bag, 'I've made a 'Happy Father's Day' card.'

I began to say, 'Jack, you need to understand…' but before I had a chance to continue he ran off with his favourite Hot Wheels car. The talk could wait. I did wonder though whether the teachers, who knew he was fatherless, would have made the same mistake if Jack's dad had been dead rather than missing-in-action.

Mind you, mistakes can easily be made. Like the time I bought pajamas for Jack's Christmas present. Knowing his love of rock music, I couldn't resist buying a pair of pajamas plastered with the image of an electric guitar and lightning bolts. However, when Jack opened his present, my heart sank as I noticed part of the image had been hidden within the packet.

It read, 'My Dad Rocks!'

Bugger.

Auntie Dan's husband, Uncle Francois, played a huge part in the boys' lives while we were in Canada. Having no children of his own, he grew especially close to Jack, who playfully jumped and climbed all over Francois during our stay, covering his bald head with kisses. Jack's fun-loving nature made him easy to love.

Uncle Francois was partly paralyzed from the polio he'd contracted as a boy and, as a result, had to use crutches or a wheelchair to get around. In spite of this, he refused to let anything slow him down and Francois' wheelchair proved to be pure pleasure for Jack. Seated on Francois' knee, Jack would shout, 'faster, faster' as the two of them whizzed around the supermarket, missing people by millimetres and knocking over displays of tinned food.

Being disabled, Francois lived with constant leg and back pain but never let this diminish what he would do for Jack. Every night, he would endure further discomfort as he sat on the cold, tiled bathroom floor entertaining Jack in his bath. When Jack was about to get out of the bath, Francois would shout for Dan to warm Jack's pajamas and towel. This was royal treatment compared with the routine at home when he would entertain himself in the shower for forty-five minutes while I prepared dinner or sat on my bed with a glass of chardonnay reading a few pages of Rachel Resnick's Love Junkie.

To strengthen Jack's relationship with Dan and Francois, I asked them to be his Godparents. Jack was oblivious to the importance of this, but I wasn't and I hugged them tightly. If anything happened to me Jack wouldn't be alone. They accepted, excited at the prospect of being part of Jack's life forever.

The only hitch was the fact I wasn't Catholic, which led to a rather awkward conversation with Father Christian when I rang to book the baptism.

'Are you Catholic?' he asked.

'No,' I replied.

'Is your husband Catholic?' he inquired.

'I haven't got a husband,' I answered.

'Is your child's father Catholic?' he continued.

'Don't know, I haven't got one of those either!'

Nothing more was said and a baptism picture book arrived in the post for Jack a few days later.

The ceremony went without a hitch, although, I spent most of the time glancing at Father Christian, who had sweat running down his nose. I felt concerned he might faint from wearing so many layers in the over-heated church and running after Jack, who after the ceremony had sprinted off with the blessed candle and was flaying it through the air, pretending to be Luke Skywalker.

As for me, watching Jack's face light up as his new Godparents picked him up and planted kisses all over his cheeks gave me goose bumps.

Now he would always be part of a family.

Chapter 3

Simone's jaw dropped when she saw the luggage I planned to take on the two buses and six trains to the annual Winter Carnival in Quebec.

'*C'est pas possible!*' Simone cried. Her eyes were fixed on my three suitcases, three smaller backpacks, one pushchair, two bags of food, one bag of toys and a red plastic sleigh.

But what could I do? There were so many extra things I had to pack for life in the snow. I was even using a sleigh for Jack, instead of trying to manoeuver a pushchair in the snow.

'Surely you don't need the sleigh?' Simone said as she looked outside at the oncoming blizzard, 'In this weather you need to take taxis.'

'I have always walked everywhere and a little snowstorm is not going to change that,' I replied.

Yes, I admit, travelling in the snow with young children and an army of suitcases was to be a grueling task. Luckily, Nanny had schooled me in lessons of fortitude. She could never afford a car so we went by bus each day in the depths of the London winter to visit my dying mother in hospital.

In spite of this, being an independent woman can be very challenging. When I sold my three-storied house to fund this trip I resolved to do it alone. I hired a truck, buckled the boys in and moved everything into my new two-bedroom apartment. At nine o'clock, two-year-old

Jack was still sitting in the truck in the rain. A bottle of milk was his only comfort. When I noticed Jack alone, lurking guilt tapped me on the shoulder. Bad mother! I hated being alone, so why hadn't I asked for help?

After packing the last box into the truck I jumped in beside Jack and said, 'I know Dale Carnegie once said, "if life gives you lemons, make lemonade" but in the words of some great Chinese philosopher, "Sometimes life just sucks!"'

Necessary items for a life in winter:
- Sleigh
- Hot chocolate
- Mittens and gloves
- Scarves and snow suits
- Sensitive toothpaste
- Kindness of strangers
- Cozy Italian restaurants
- Camera
- Physiotherapy for back problems
- Saint Christopher (to save us from being hit by falling ice shafts).

Although my ridiculous pile of luggage was unmanageable, I was pleasantly surprised to discover that seeing a mother struggle to manoeuvre two children and ten pieces of baggage prompted strangers to stop and help.

As Marco, Jack and I arrived at our first train, I tried to keep an eye on the boys who had already jumped on. I managed to hold the door open with my heaviest suitcase as I heaved the pushchair, sleigh and the other two suitcases onto the train before the doors closed. Numerous men stood watching my struggle, proving that chivalry is officially extinct. Thankfully, a petite Asian woman started to heave my obscenely weighty suitcase onto the train. I might be independent but I can still appreciate generosity.

Female compassion rescued us again during our trip to Quebec as we dragged ourselves through Montreal's metro system. Most of the stations lacked escalators or elevators, so, as I sat with the boys in the crowded carriage surrounded by our baggage, I calmly contemplated how we were going to execute the numerous platform changes using the stairs.

I was seated opposite a woman who eagerly introduced herself as Belinda. She noticed our accents and luggage and wanted to know where we had come from and what our travel plans were. She told me she was en-route to the cinema on a rare day off from both work and child minding. Her trendy denim jacket, tight pants and high heels made me imagine her excitement at ditching her domestic clothes for this much-anticipated day of freedom. I could certainly relate to that.

She noticed the puzzled look on my face as I studied the metro's map and asked, 'Do you need some help?'

'Please,' I replied. 'This map is so confusing. I have no idea how to get to Gare Central, where we are catching our next train to Quebec.'

Belinda looked at my face.

She looked at the luggage.

She looked at the map.

She looked back at the luggage.

'There are three platform changes. I can go to the film another day. Let me take you there.'

In addition to meeting generous people like Belinda, I discovered that train travel also created opportunities to interact with all sorts of people that I would not normally have occasion to meet.

Enter Sergio.

Sergio rolled his drinks and food cart up to my seat shortly after the train left Montreal for Vieux Quebec. He didn't seem to care that he was blocking the aisle as he stood chatting to me for the next thirty minutes. I listened to stories about his mother's health problems and tried to help him decide on the colour of his bathroom tiles for the house he was renovating. I began to notice the angry glares from other passengers who were waiting for him to continue down the aisle. I was also taken aback when, in front of everyone around me, he proceeded to tell me how beautiful I was. Although this was flattering, I recoiled into my seat in a bid to hide. Those who overheard his comments now sat staring, waiting for my reaction. Marco sat quietly grinning.

I must confess that I found Sergio quite attractive, too. He wasn't tall, dark and handsome but then that's never been important to me. He was actually bald, a trait I've been attracted to since my twenties. In fact, a few years earlier I had a student crush on one of my bald university professors. Instead of taking notes while he lectured on the subject of French Cinema I would fantasize about the bald head that stood fifty feet in front of me.

My attraction to the unconventional will come as no surprise to those who know me well, as I have often embraced the quirkiness in people. In fact, paralyzed limbs, oversized jackets that hide a man's hands and limps – just to name a few – have not bothered me in the past, or at least, not in the beginning.

So, when the very bald Sergio later invited Jack and me (Marco was busy playing chess with a neighboring passenger) into the first-class car for a glass of wine I jumped at the chance. We sat chatting while Jack looked out the window, excited by the snowy landscape. Since the train was overheated, I removed my jacket. Noticing the freckles on my arm, Sergio declared that he too had similar moles. Next, Sergio was removing his jacket and taking off his shirt to show me his! I didn't have the heart to tell him that many of the marks on his arms were liver spots due to the fact that he was considerably older than me. Luckily, there were other train employees sitting opposite, otherwise who knows what body parts Sergio might have revealed.

As Marco, Jack and I left the train at Vieux Quebec we were confronted by a blizzard. I pushed the boys into a waiting taxi just as Sergio tapped me on the shoulder.

'My mother once told me that people come and go in your life, but only a few will leave footprints in your heart. You, Rebekah, are one of them.'

Yes, the world was full of new friends waiting to be encountered, some for the duration of a train ride, and some for life.

'Mum, hurry up,' Marco yelled from inside the taxi.

I lent over and gave Sergio a quick kiss on his cheek. His skin felt cold and slightly damp from the snow that was striking our faces.

'I must go. I promised the boys I would take them sliding as soon as we arrived.'

'I understand. Have lots of fun with your boys.'

'I can't wait,' I replied, as I jumped into the taxi with the boys, who were excited, like me, to be in a real snowstorm.

Chapter 4

I had not seen Vy for over two years, so I was shocked to see how her body had shrunk as a result of leukemia. Vy was the daughter of Au Petit Hotel's Cambodian proprietor and she smiled warmly as she greeted us and showed us to our hotel room. We had become close during previous stays over the last eight years.

I tried to seem unruffled, but was upset to notice such deterioration in the health of Vy, who was only a couple of years older than me. She covered her bald head with an assortment of headscarves and hats. Grey skin stretched tautly over her skeletal body. An inability to sleep had created cavernous black bags under her eyes. Every day when we returned to the hotel she would be sitting wrapped in blankets, having developed a heightened sensitivity to the cold. I did not know how to react, or what to say.

Although she was exhausted by her weekly chemotherapy, she never spoke about her illness with self-pity and she always smiled at the guests as she huddled behind the reception desk. Many nights, Vy cooked extra Vietnamese noodles to share with us. She had no partner or children so I think she enjoyed our company. After the meal she would sit quietly in her armchair and ask me to tell her all about New Zealand, a place she said that she had always wanted to visit. Whenever the freezing weather prevented us from walking, she insisted on driving us around town. Even though she was barely able to move, she often babysat Jack at night so Marco and I could enjoy grown-up outings together.

One morning at Au Petit Hotel I was enjoying a rare quiet moment reading in bed whilst the boys watched cartoons on the television. I had only five more pages of Leonard Cohen's *Book of Longing* left when I heard Vy screaming, 'Get out of here!' followed by the sound of a loud thud. Looking out the window, I was astounded to see Vy throwing a woman's luggage onto the snow-covered street. I dashed downstairs and found Vy back in her seat, wrapped in her blankets. Her soft voice returned as she explained how she had found a guest smoking in her room – an offence, which warranted a 100 dollar fine to cover the cost of cleaning. When the guest said she had no money to pay the fine, Vy, all thirty kilos of her, threw the woman out on the street along with her luggage. As a taxi stopped in front of the hotel Vy ran out shouting to the driver, 'Don't take her! She has no money. She won't pay you!'

The taxi swiftly departed.

The woman stood there speechless and stranded.

Au Petit Hotel was cosy. The small narrow building stood four-stories high, and since we were on the top floor, I had to puff my way up the steep circular staircase multiple times a day. Almost 100 years old, the original plaster was falling off the thin walls in places, which I thought added to the overall charm. The rooms were so small that Marco had to use the bathroom for quiet space away from his noisy brother. He'd sit on the toilet for hours engrossed in Christopher Paolini's *Eragon*.

We began each day at Au Petit Hotel with breakfast in bed: fresh melon, grapes, warm buttery croissants, wholemeal toast and marmalade, freshly squeezed orange juice and percolated coffee – all for the grand sum of two dollars fifty. After our morning feast, we headed out most days to the Plains of Abraham, a large park near our hotel, to find the best slopes for tobogganing, which I loved as much as the boys. By the end I'd be limping, aching and out of breath, but the mixture of screaming and laughter as we whizzed down the icy slopes compensated well for the pain that followed and left us eager to return the following day.

One practical feature of Au Petit Hotel was its location in relation to the Winter Carnival. This year's carnival was special – not only would it have its annual seventeen days of festivities, it would also celebrate 400 years since the founding of the city. In winter, its snow-covered cobblestone streets lined with hand-crafted stone buildings and horse-drawn carriages evoked an enchanted fairy-tale scene. Au Petit Hotel was also metres from award-winning restaurants and thrilling winter activities like the Glissard, a steep slide made of ice with hundreds of lights draped around it. The boys and I stood behind a queue of dads waiting to hire wooden toboggans to pull their kids to the top of the slide while the mums stood at the bottom taking photographs and cheering. Jack sat on top of the toboggan as I heaved him to the top of the ice-slide. Marco trudged beside, egging me on. I smiled, trying not to let on that I wanted to give up halfway. Icy wind whipped our faces as we arrived at the summit, where we boarded as a threesome and screamed with fear and delight for what seemed like only five seconds until we came to a sudden halt at the bottom. We had not even disembarked before Jack yelled, 'Do it again, do it again!' There was no way I could refuse. On our second ascent, my trembling legs and shortness of breath caused me to keep stopping to rest. The burly men towing their sleighs passed me with ease.

'I wish I had a daddy to pull me,' Jack suddenly said.

I moved over to the left so another father could pass us by.

'Look at the pretty lights on the château Jack,' I said, trying to change the subject, but my eyes watered. How could I tell him that I secretly wanted that, too? I quickly brushed my tears away.

Sensing my distress, Marco offered to take over the chore, but when he was almost at the top he slipped. All I could do was shut my eyes, hoping for the best and listen to the screams of both boys as they and the sleigh slid to the bottom at full speed. Thankfully, no bones were broken. Even though Marco protested that he would hold on tighter next time, I grabbed the rope to make sure Jack was safe inside and began to trudge upward once more.

Marco's offer to pull the sleigh was typical of his desire to help me with chores that most fathers do. This was clearly the case when I went into labour with Jack. My contractions started during the night and intensified about five o'clock in the morning. I didn't want to disturb anybody at such an early hour, so I packed eight-year-old Marco and my suitcase into the car and set off to the hospital. Luckily, the contractions coincided with the red lights along the way, allowing me to stop and breathe deeply with my eyes shut. Marco informed me when the light turned green and off we went again, until the next contraction and the next red light. It was Marco who lugged my suitcase into the hospital, while I parked the car.

If I hadn't been in such pain at the time, I would have told Marco how grateful I was for his help; I just wish he hadn't needed to do it.

Since our separation eight years ago, I have worked hard at fostering the boys' relationship with Marco's dad, Stephan, and Stephan's girlfriend, Margot, whenever we see them at family gatherings. I have encouraged taking family photos together and sharing dinners. Once, we even shared a room at Au Petit Hotel while on holiday in Quebec – though I must admit when the lights went out I regretted my decision. However the boys' happiness has always been my priority, even if it has meant ignoring my feelings of unease at times.

The advantage of maintaining a civil relationship with my ex-husband meant I was able to call Stephan, who lived part-time in Quebec with Margot, and ask him to join us at Parc Valcartier, a winter playground of 5000 inner tubes and huge snowy hills. Stephan's help during our outing was a welcome reprieve. We could now give the boys more individual attention. Immediately, Marco and his dad darted off to adventurous slides like the almost-vertical Everest, while Jack and I set off for the beginners' area. Yet, even the gentle slopes were intimidating and I soon realised I had no way of returning to the bottom other than by descending on the tyre. Holding onto Jack, we slid down on the shared tyre both of us howling. Later on, with adrenalin pumping, Jack and I abandoned the easy slopes to scream our way down the almost-vertical Hurricane slide twenty-seven times in a row.

Fun times in the snow left us starving. Luckily, there were many gourmet restaurants in Quebec, though, as we discovered, not all of them were child-friendly. All eyes focused on us as we entered the silent dining room of Aux Anciens Canadien, dating from 1675, with style and food from that era. I imagined children of that period were to be seen and not heard, in contrast to Jack who sat at the table repeatedly yelling, 'I want to go home.' To make matters worse, after spending ten minutes in the overheated dining room he decided to remove his smelly, wet winter boots and throw a sock across the restaurant. It landed two centimeters from a woman's bowl of pea soup. Luckily, she was sharing her table with her two teenage boys and glanced back with understanding. We raced through our food that night, and I went to bed dreaming about booking a 'no kids' retreat in Tahiti in eight months time.

New Year's Eve in Quebec was keenly anticipated, not only because it was part of the city's 400th centenary, but also because the previous New Year was spent drinking cheap sparkling wine alone in my pajamas on the couch and in bed well before midnight. Unable to sleep I had begun to chant Mae West's words, 'I'm single because I was born that way. I'm single because I was born that way,' but it was no good, I just couldn't help feeling sorry for myself. So, the idea of a midnight party in the snow with lots of others in Quebec one year on felt romantic and exciting. Of course, catering for two young boys in tow swiftly destroyed that fantasy.

Nevertheless we dined at Au Parmesan, an Italian eatery filled with balloons, laughter and revelry. Hosts Luigi and César welcomed us warmly with, *'Ciao Bella'*, but otherwise the evening started badly. Our booking had been misplaced and being New Year's Eve the place was packed. On seeing my extreme disappointment, the maître'd managed to squeeze us onto one of the tiniest tables I had ever seen, right next to the cashier. At first I was relieved but when a male patron bumped me on his way to pay the bill, I stabbed the roof of my mouth with my fork. Then a clumsy waiter knocked my arm, sending my Chianti flying across the red-and-white checked tablecloth. With his head held high, the waiter rushed past not giving me a second glance.

As Jack and Marco licked their plates of spaghetti bolognaise clean, my ruffled feathers were soothed by an accordion player who edged towards us between the tables. Then, I watched the boys devour two bowls of creamy cassata dessert.

It wasn't quite the relaxing New Year's Eve meal I had envisaged, although being jammed into such a loud and bustling space helped us feel part of the liveliness.

Fed and energized, we joined thousands of other partygoers on the cold snowy night to watch live music in Place d'Youville, the heart of Quebec City. Later, we retreated to the comfort of a coffee bar to warm our numb toes. Sipping a hot chocolate, I watched Marco plow his way through a mango sorbet.

'Do you know it's minus-ten degrees outside?' I asked him.

'Yeah, why?'

'Just wanted to make sure.'

Back at the hotel, we layered ourselves in warm clothes and hastily returned to secure a prime view of the festivities that were kicking off the hour leading up to midnight. However, there was a problem. It was only nine o'clock. In sub-zero temperatures, the chill mixed with a strong wind felt like needles stabbing our faces. What was I thinking? Jack finally cried himself to sleep (perhaps from hypothermia rather than fatigue) in his red sleigh and Marco was cantankerous. Eventually, we surrendered and tackled the twenty-minute climb up the steep hill to return to the warmth of the hotel room yet again.

It's not in my nature to give up, so, just before midnight, I re-bundled a sleeping Jack in the hotel's woollen blanket and into his sleigh. Marco protested but I dragged them back to the snow-lined streets to join the revelry. At midnight fireworks lit up the sky and Jack stirred enough to notice the 'pretty lights' then he returned to sleep. A hug with Marco on the strike of midnight shifted to a snowball fight. When we weren't able to feel our fingers any longer, Marco and I linked arms and ambled our way back to the hotel pulling Jack through the narrow cobblestone streets with the thousands of others, chanting, 'Ole ole ole ole. Ole, ole, ole, ole.' Jack slept on, completely oblivious.

'Happy New Year, Marco,' I said as I jumped into my warm bed back at the hotel.

'What Mum? I'm sleepy,' Marco replied.

'That was my best New Year's Eve ever,' I answered.

He was already asleep. I, on the other hand, was wide awake, only this New Year's Eve I couldn't stop smiling.

Advantages of Living with Snow:

- *Tire d'érable* – hot, melted maple syrup poured onto snow and rolled over a stick as it hardens.
- Rosy cheeks when outside in the cold (great for photographs!).
- The relief of returning to a warm hotel.
- Making snowmen, igloos and having snowball battles with my boys.
- Excitement created by sliding down slopes on sleds, inner tubes and bottoms.
- Stunning scenery for photos as a result of a 60-year record 3.42 metre snowfall.
- Doing 360-degree turns in a car with ex-husband – kids love this.
- Vigorous exercise pushing Jack's pushchair.
- Meeting kind and empathetic people who lifted the pushchair when stuck in snow.
- Ditching the pushchair and using a sled.

Disadvantages of Living with Snow:

- Liable to be stuck in snow with a pushchair during a 60-year record snowfall of 3.42 metres.
- Straining your back and bottom in an attempt to push a stroller in the snow.
- Holding a distraught toddler as the cold burns his cheeks.
- Doing 360-degree turns in a car with ex-husband (mothers don't love this).
- Walking the streets in fear, following a near-death experience when a colossal shaft of ice fell from the eave of a roof, missing me by millimeters.
- *Tire d'érable* – because of its negative effect on my waistline.
- Having Jack wake up and ask to go to the beach.

I had high expectations for our time in Quebec. I knew the boys would love the sliding, snowball fights and outdoor skating, but, on our eighth day, an unexpected blizzard hit. We found ourselves seriously tested inside the cramped hotel room for three days. I tried to entertain the boys with cards and television, however there were only so many episodes of *Deadliest Catch* that even I could endure.

By the third day, I was beginning to question whether the new experiences I had dreamed of on this world trip were going to happen. Not only were we watching too much television, life felt far too safe.

Going crazy with my boys in a hotel room would have amused the skeptics, who prior to my departure predicted that travelling with two kids would be nightmarish. Still isn't life as a parent arduous on a daily basis, even at home? Some might say, 'Same chores, different place.' I say, why not experience the challenges that come with parenting in new places, whilst meeting interesting people and not knowing what each new day will bring? In reality, my adrenalin rush so far was being stimulated from visits to theme parks and festivals. Maybe Europe would turn out to be more intrepid.

Luckily, the wind dropped in time for the first day of the Winter Carnival. After three days of confinement we stepped outside into twenty-five centimeters of snow that had fallen overnight. The blanket of white looked magical, but passing local residents digging out their cars reminded me how lucky I was. For many months ahead I would have no mundane responsibilities.

Over the next few days, we watched dog-sled races and went snow-rafting over huge hills of snow that propelled us into the air at high speed. To calm my nerves I drank thick, creamy alcoholic liquor served in a glass made of ice. In the evenings we listened to live music, watched dance performances and firework displays. Walking back to the hotel each night we were enchanted by the Carnival's Ice Palace. Illuminated by coloured lights that gently glowed through the walls of ice we stood transfixed, awaiting the exact moment that the palace changed colour.

'Blue, I want blue,' cried Jack.

'No, it's going to be green,' Marco laughed.

I wished for pink. And pink it was.

Six hours spent outside each day in a minus-twenty-degree temperature would end with the comfort of hot grilled sausages, wrapped in bread and topped with sweet fried onions, mustard and ketchup.

With everything going smoothly the last thing I was expecting was a call from my Auntie Elizabeth in England telling me, 'Doris is dead.'

PART 3

England (briefly)

Chapter 5

Bruce Springsteen sang, *I Wanna Marry You* on the stereo as my sailor boyfriend David got down on one knee and held out an emerald and diamond engagement ring.

'Rebekah, will you marry me?'

'Of course!' I said, throwing my arms around him.

I was seventeen years old.

Luckily, Nanny knew best and swiftly shipped me off to London to train as a chef and complete a two-year City & Guilds' Diploma in Professional Cookery. Even though I knew Nanny was trying to get me away from my new fiancé, which ought to have made me mad, I went, accepting that she was right. Lots of heartache followed, but that's another story.

The course was in North London, so Nanny asked her ex-husband, my grandfather, if I could stay with him, his new wife and two sons who lived near the college. I begged Nanny to find somewhere else for me live. As a child, I had despised my grandfather, because in my mind his departure from the family home had ultimately led to my mum's death. My mother had her first heart attack at the age of sixteen, the year he left Nanny for another woman. He had broken my mother and my nan's heart.

My instincts proved to be correct.

My bedroom was the only room in their house where the radiator was never turned on. Whenever the family left the house I secretly spent time in their heated rooms. When I heard them coming up the stairs to the front door I would rush back and lie in my bed shivering, wishing I was back home in New Zealand with the warmth of Nanny's arms around me.

Every morning I had to venture outside into the frost to retrieve the milk for my breakfast. Grandfather insisted it be left in a glass on a windowsill outside the house, so as not to wake his precious pet Labrador that slept in the kitchen. Then when I arrived home exhausted after a long day of cooking, Grandfather would stand outside the bathroom and time my showers, allowing five minutes, which he only permitted every second day.

To fund my education I went straight from cooking school each day to work as a waitress at a Chinese restaurant until well after midnight. Too young to know better, and because other alternatives cost too much, I let myself be driven home each night by the restaurant's manager. I felt terrified watching him gulp down a shot each of eight bottles of spirits before getting into the car drunk. I asked Grandfather to help me out – to lend me some money or pick me up from the restaurant. He always refused.

To relieve my financial pressure I asked Grandfather to apply for the orphan's benefit Nanny had previously received, so he could give me a weekly allowance. He told me that he applied but was turned down, so I had no choice but to keep working nights.

Months after leaving his home I asked my aunt Doris to apply for the same benefit, because I thought maybe there had been a mix-up with his application.

Doris rang the Department of Social Welfare and the woman who answered the telephone put her on hold while she made some enquiries.

'Are you still there, Mrs Green?' the woman asked.

'Yes,' Doris replied.

'Great! I have good news. The orphan's benefit can be easily transferred into your name from the previous recipient, Rebekah's grandfather, Harold Tyler.'

The hardship I endured in London was worth the outcome of qualifying as a chef, during which time I won 'Top Student Award' two years running and was fourth in the world for my final City & Guilds' exam. Nanny had taught me to be strong, yet I spent the majority of my free time as a homesick, lovesick teenager.

Most weekends I would travel by train to the little village of East Horsley in Surrey and stay with my great-aunt Doris, Nanny's sister. Doris always gave me a smothering hug. She would then sweep me off to her local pub for a ploughman's lunch and a cold glass of shandy. Stomachs contented, we strolled back home through the woods that were bursting with bluebells. As soon as we entered her two-bedroom brick bungalow, Doris flew into preparations for a roast beef dinner with old-fashioned Yorkshire pudding, which we ate in her formal dining room. Over dinner, Doris would tell me how much she missed Nanny. She often expressed her concerns for our wellbeing in New Zealand, upon hearing that Kiwi children went to school in bare feet.

'How uncivilised,' Doris would argue, when I told her that children loved the freedom of feeling the warm pavement under their soles. She was never convinced.

Before bed and with bellies full, I would help her lay the kitchen table with a blue-and-white gingham tablecloth, teacups, plates, cutlery, butter and marmalade for breakfast in the morning. Although the table looked pretty, I wished I had been setting an extra place for Nanny, as I had done so many times as a little girl when we had come to Doris's for holidays before moving to New Zealand.

With the table set, I would hop into the stiff, starched sheets of the spare bed with a hot water bottle, pull up the feather eiderdown and drift off to sleep, no longer homesick, that is, until my return to Grandfather's each Sunday.

Although I dreaded returning to London, I hoped that one day Grandfather might tell me stories about my mother when she was a young girl. That never happened. Instead, on the second of September, my mum's birthday and one year after I arrived, I told my grandfather that I was going to lay flowers beside my mum's grave. He stopped me and placed some money in my hand to put towards the flowers for his dead daughter. Once outside I opened my hand to reveal a single fifty-pence coin. I left my grandfather's house two weeks later and never spoke to him again.

Where did I turn? To Doris, of course.

'Do not come to England! There is crime, poverty, immigration problems and a dreadful Government,' Doris wrote to me when she heard I was planning my trip with the boys. The England she had known growing up had changed, and she did not approve.

I chose to ignore her comments and was looking forward to introducing the boys to Doris during the next leg of our trip to England. I hoped she was still keen to see us too, regardless of the state of Britain.

I was also especially intent on asking Doris all the questions I hadn't had the chance to ask Nanny before she died: questions about Nanny's youth, about my mum, and about my unknown father whom my mother had met during a holiday in San Sebastian, Spain, when she was nineteen. It wasn't to be – two days after arriving back at Simone's from the Winter Festival in Quebec, I received a phone call from England. In between sobs, Auntie Elizabeth, Nanny's niece, managed only the words, 'Doris is dead.'

I was playing cards with Marco and Jack when the phone rang and was stunned with the news.

'Mum, hurry up. It's your turn.'

I felt numb.

Walking to the table, I picked up my cards and let Marco win, before running to my room and closing the door, trying to shut out the sounds of the boys' laughter and the lingering smell of Simone's homemade meatballs that I had wolfed down moments ago.

I suddenly felt sick.

Doris was dead.

Auntie Dan offered to look after the boys for as long as I needed.

Two days later I was on a plane to England.

Orson Welles once said, 'There are only two emotions on a plane: boredom and terror.' I interpret his word 'terror' as the dread a mother feels travelling with a two year old. It was more than eight years since I had travelled alone and despite the sad circumstances, it was liberating to have a respite from responsibility, so I was happy to embrace Welles' idea of boredom during my flight to London.

I didn't care that the grumpy-looking hostess greeted me with a forced smile; the cheap pinot noir tasted smooth as I gulped down glass after glass; the small, lumpy seat felt comfortable as I stretched out and pulled the itchy blanket over my tired body. Watching the movies on the tiny screen without having to frequently push the pause button was a pleasure and the pale, cold chicken casserole and wilted salad greens tasted positively gourmet. Everything about this flight was a treat, without the usual interruptions.

I felt as if I had all the time in the world and looked around at the other passengers nearby. I imagined each person's story and where they might be going. Was there a lover waiting, or was this voyage a distraction from a broken heart? Was this journey the beginning of a new life? Or, was their trip an escape from reality like mine?

I noticed a hunched over old lady in a tweed suit who reminded me of Doris and suddenly felt embarrassed about my curiosity and excitement. Here I was lapping up my freedom on my way to England for Doris's funeral. The Rodrigues' had offered me the time alone and

I had grabbed it. Did I go to the funeral for Doris? Or, did I go for myself? Why had I bothered to pack my hair straighteners and red lipstick along with my black dress?

Standing over Doris's coffin triggered many precious memories. There was the sweet smell of the marmalade that she bottled each year, the ticking of her grandfather clock, the crisp feel of her starched sheets on the bed where I slept, the cold touch of her leather gloves when she held my face in her hands to say goodbye and the sadness I felt when I left her, along with the happiness I felt every time I returned.

Alongside Nanny, Doris played a significant role in my early childhood. Although I didn't have a mother and a father, I never lacked love and laughter while in their care. I can still picture the two of them standing outside Doris's brick bungalow unable to get the key into the front door because they couldn't stop laughing at a rude joke Doris had told. It was wonderful to see two eighty-year-old women laughing together, even if it did lead me to make a mental note to stock up on incontinence pads.

In spite of Doris's great sense of humour, she could also be formidable. It was she who first taught me about manners. I will always remember the time we went to Sainsbury's supermarket. I was thirteen years old. After paying, Doris looked at the cashier and said in her regal voice, 'Pardon?' The young supermarket employee looked up at her, not understanding and replied, 'I didn't say anything.' In an elongated, exaggerated tone, Doris responded, 'Oh, I thought you said thank you.' As a teenager I felt horrified. As an adult I began mimicking her.

Doris's words were especially harsh when it came to my choice of boyfriends. Anyone would have been better in Doris's mind than Pete, my boyfriend, who had ruined her Christmas twenty-odd years ago when I was eighteen.

I had met Pete during my chef's training in London. Pete was a tall, lanky, twenty-four-year old bad boy. I was a young, naïve romantic who thought she could heal the damage done to him from years of abuse he had received as a child living in a dysfunctional family. How was he bad? Let's just say that when I was living in a high-rise council flat in a dodgy part of London, after leaving my grandfather's, mine was the only flat in the complex not burgled – Pete happened to be mates with all the local robbers.

Soon after I met Pete I went to stay with Doris for the Christmas break. Doris had made it quite clear when she met Pete earlier she did not think he was suitable boyfriend material. She had dreamed that I might meet a nice young doctor one day and like her, live in a nice bungalow in Surrey. She certainly did not want me married to some bad boy Londoner who lived in a Bedford van and rarely showered. Nonetheless, she endured him, praying I would come to my senses and settle down with a nice lad eventually.

However, Doris refused to have 'that smelly boy' stay in her clean, starched sheets for the holiday, but she compromised and invited Pete for Boxing Day lunch. This was an important event for Doris. Neighbours were invited, the table was set with the finest of crockery and silver and a big roast turkey lunch was cooked to perfection. Mr and Mrs Thorpe from next door arrived at noon. Mr and Mrs Hadley knocked on the door a few minutes later.

Pete never arrived.

Everyone, including Pete, knew that you did not let down Doris and as the minutes of his no-show turned to hours I became worried. My anxiety increased seeing Doris scowl at me as she carved the turkey, knowing she felt humiliated by Pete's absence in front of the neighbours she was trying to impress.

I tried ringing Pete after the pea and ham soup.

I rang again following the turkey, roast potatoes and gravy.

I tried once more after Doris's homemade trifle.

There was never an answer.

Eventually I spoke to one of his friends, who reluctantly told me that on Christmas Eve, Pete and his younger brother, John, had gone to their local pub, The Cherry Tree, for a few drinks. A fight had broken out and John was arrested.

Being the protective older brother that he was, Pete was determined to 'save John.' Problem was, he had no transport.

Bad choice #1 – he decided to steal a car.

Bad choice #2 – he sped past a police car en route to the station.

This earned him an even faster ride to the cop shop – handcuffed and in the back of a police car. As a result, John was released and Pete spent Christmas in Wormwood Scrubs, one of the scariest prisons in Britain. In a state of shock I told Doris the truth – in front of the neighbours. She was speechless – until the neighbours left.

Being the young, eager-to-please girlfriend that I was, I took the train to London the following morning to support Pete during his court hearing. I stood in a lilac twin set borrowed from Doris, in the hope of 'looking sweet and innocent' – as Doris put it. She may have disliked the idea of me dating Pete, but she hated the idea of me going out with a 'convicted Pete' more.

From the dock Pete gave me a huge smile, as if to say, 'Thanks babe.' I, on the other hand, just about vomited as Pete revealed a huge toothless grin. From the moment I met Pete I always felt there was something strange about his teeth. There was a little gap where the top of his teeth met the gum. I stared at his mouth as he spoke to the judge. Oh God. False teeth? No! Really? I knew that Pete's lawyer was speaking but I wasn't able to focus on the hearing any more. Had he worn false teeth all that time? How could I have not known? I guessed that in prison they were considered a weapon and confiscated.

Pete turned and smiled at me again. I wanted to jump back onto that train, straight to the starched sheets and comforting arms of

Auntie Doris. Instead I chose to stay, smile sweetly and pretend I hadn't noticed his gummy grin.

While Doris's body had become stooped and shrivelled by the time she had reached her nineties, her mind and will remained strong. Doris was determined to look after herself in her own home until the day she died. True to this resolution she continued cooking family luncheons until her death at the age of ninety-two. Her table was always set with bone china, linen napkins and silver, even when she ate alone. Heavy ceramic serving dishes were filled to the brim with succulent roast meat, piping-hot fresh carrots, broccoli and potatoes with thickened homemade gravy. Wine accompanied the meal in sparkling crystal glasses, which were a wedding present. When appetites were well satisfied, Doris would present a homemade trifle layered with light sponge cake, dry sherry, creamy homemade custard, fresh fruit and sweetened whipped cream.

Sadly, Doris's highly steadfast character often drove away the very people she loved most. She frequently criticised people without knowing the full picture. This was the case years earlier when Doris thought her brother Bill's laughter was directed at her when he'd actually been chuckling about a story on the radio. Doris refused to believe him and did not to speak to him for over thirty years.

During the funeral service, the vicar seemed to understand Doris's deep convictions and moral standards when she gave her address, 'As you all know, Doris didn't hold with divorce and parenthood outside marriage horrified her.' My Auntie Elizabeth, cousins Sarah and Caroline and I all looked at each other and cringed. She was talking about us.

Eleven years earlier, Doris sent nasty letters to me when I told her that as well as becoming engaged to Stephan in Paris, I was also pregnant.

'How could you have done this to Nanny?' she wrote. 'You are a disgrace to the family.'

I argued that at least Stephan had proposed beforehand, but that didn't make any difference.

Consequently, when I found I was pregnant with Jack, the thought of telling Doris mortified me. I decided to express all the negative comments I anticipated before she had the chance. I cringed as I wrote telling her of my 'reckless, negligent, irresponsible and foolish behaviour.' Then I considered writing another saying, 'although this baby isn't planned, I am so happy Marco will have a sibling. He won't be alone as I have always been as a child.' But I didn't change the words. Instead, I posted the original to Doris. I felt sick writing about my unborn child like this. However, it worked. Doris had no come back – I had said it all.

Even though I was grateful for Doris's withheld reprimand, deep down I knew that this was not going to be enough. I had to do something else. I needed Doris to love my baby son.

I wrote to Doris again, this time asking if I could name my baby Jack, after her husband who had died thirty years earlier. Perhaps this would help.

Uncle Jack was the one subject that could truly soften Doris. Jack had died from a malignant tumor on his nose. The tumor was caused by a mosquito bite that he received on the island of Malta, while serving his country during World War II. They had spent six years apart because of the war.

During their separation Doris's love for him never wavered and they married on his return, only to discover that they had left it too late to have children. However, just having each other seemed enough for both of them. They were perfectly balanced. Jack was a quiet man whereas Doris was commanding and opinionated. She was the boss. Yet, he adored her and she cherished him.

My cousin Caroline found two brown envelopes in Doris's handbag after her death, which she gave to me. The first contained a pile of black-and-white photos taken on Doris and Jack's honeymoon in the south of France, while the second enclosed the poem *You and I* that Jack had written to Doris and which she had carried every day since his death. I read it immediately:

You and I

We'll not be sad
Not ever,
You and I
Always be glad
For the sun and wind and sky,
Glad for the dusk and dawn, the day's gay light
And thankful for the privacy of night.

Glad when I look at you
And you at me
And while a secret smile
No others see.
Glad for the sweep of music
Through the air
And for the wind's soft fingers
In our hair.

For all things glad,
For sun and wind and sky –
But mostly for each other
You and I.

I placed the poem back inside the brown envelope and put the photographs and poem into my handbag. I wondered whether I might ever find a loving man like Uncle Jack, to write poetry about his love for me.

When my baby Jack was born I hoped that during his childhood he would spend time with Doris learning about Uncle Jack's kind and loving qualities. Since Jack had no father of his own to admire, Uncle Jack could be his 'special person.' Instead of sitting quietly when his classmates talked about their fathers and what they did for a job, Jack could proudly tell his school friends, 'Well, my Uncle Jack spent six years fighting in World War II and then came back to marry his sweetheart, who had waited all that time for him.' This way, Jack could be part of his great-uncle's legacy.

In spite of this, when I visited Doris's house before her funeral to quietly say goodbye, I discovered how Doris had really felt about my son being born out of wedlock. Although she had agreed to my naming my baby Jack and had acknowledged my Jack in letters sent with jumpers she had knitted for his birthday, the numerous photos of him that I had sent her were nowhere to be seen. Plenty of other family photos were displayed on her mahogany sideboard. I eventually found Jack's photos hidden in a chest of drawers and gently placed them into my bag. My chest felt tight. It felt as though, in a bid to keep up appearances with neighbours and friends, Doris had denied Jack's existence. How could she have been so unkind? I was angry. My beautiful Jack deserved to be on show with all the others.

In the living room I took a silver-framed photograph of Uncle Jack from the sideboard and placed it in my handbag next to my Jack's photographs. Uncle Jack would look perfect on Jack's blue chest of drawers back home.

Was a photograph enough for Jack? Perhaps not. Nonetheless, it was more than I had growing up without a father. Yet, focusing on Jack's needs made me think of my own, and although I felt it was important for Jack to have people from his past like Uncle Jack, to guide him, perhaps it was more important to teach Jack to live fully in the present. This was my job.

PART 4

Canada

Chapter 6

Do you remember our trip to Quebec for the Winter Festival? Well, there's something I neglected to mention. That's partly because the significance of the event was not fully understood by me at the time. It has to do with a certain male passenger who was travelling on the train we took back to Montreal. So, let me take you back to that winter's day and our three-hour train journey on a Monday morning.

Exhausted after hours of sledding in Quebec City and then hauling our luggage out of the taxi, through the revolving doors, across one end of the station to the other, up the sloped flooring into the waiting room, down the entire platform and onto the train, I slumped into my seat hoping to relax for the next three hours. Wishful thinking. Marco and Jack immediately began to squabble over who would sit next to the window. I could feel negative vibes from onlookers. Thankfully, the conductor heard the commotion and offered the boys kitset cardboard trains, which they eagerly began to assemble.

I relaxed in my seat listening to Leonard Cohen's A *Thousand Kisses Deep* on my iPod. The snow-covered countryside passed and fell away into the distance and as I heard Jack yell, 'Toot toot!' I noticed a male passenger staring at me from a few seat rows away.

Perhaps this stranger was looking at someone else. He couldn't possibly be looking at me. When was the last time I'd done my hair? Indeed, amazing as it seemed, the man on the train was gazing straight at me. I flashed him a smile. He instantly smiled back. Could this be my *Before Sunrise* moment, when Ethan Hawke first sets eyes on the beautiful Julie Delpy?

'Mum, Marco's broken my train!'

Guess not.

Still, the train had a long way to go.

I casually looked at my reflection in the carriage's window and flattened my hair slightly. I smoothed down my red sweater, pulling it tight across my chest. A little pushup here. A little tuck down there. Then I looked up just to check. Yes, he was still watching me, a gentle smile across his lips. I felt the stirrings of some long lost romance. I had forgotten how good it felt to attract a man's attention. It was over three years since I was last held in a man's arms. From time to time, I allow myself to daydream about such things, including having a good old-fashioned kiss (maybe I should stop watching re-runs of *Casablanca*), but I quickly reject them. I had washing to be done, children to pick up, hungry kids to feed. I didn't have time for love.

Or did I?

I once went on a blind date with a guy called Joe who told me over the phone that he worked in the arts. I became excited by the prospect of meeting someone cultured, a man who might appreciate Pablo Neruda, Leonard Cohen or Ravel, or a lover who might write novels like me. So, when Joe and I met and he told me he was a clown I wanted to sue him for misrepresentation. I'm sure the five-year-olds appreciated his talent, but I needed more from a man than the ability to create balloon animals and squirt water in my eye.

I've had plenty of opportunities to go on dates, but I have chosen to remain alone. No one ever seemed to be quite 'right'. There was always an impediment: men who wanted to be the head of the house, had nervous sweat issues, or showed the rim of their toupee.

Friends have also tried to match make. On one occasion I went out with a man I nicknamed 'Mr Snapper' who showed up on a first date carrying four fillets of snapper he had caught that morning. Of course I accepted the bag of fish, which I threw into the freezer before leaving. The ever pervading smell of fish didn't help ignite the fire that night, especially when he inquired on our way home, 'So we're not going up Mount Victoria for a snog?'

A few days later, Mr Snapper rang offering me another four fillets of fish. When Marco and I pulled up outside his home, this fifty-seven-year-old appeared wearing obscenely short shorts along with a bright green Victoria Bitter branded t-shirt. The cut off-sleeves revealed his extremely hairy arms and chest. I grabbed the fish, thanked him and sped off. Once we were a safe distance away Marco remarked, 'I can see why you didn't fancy him, Mum.' Too bad – because the fish was really good.

Another time I tried internet dating. I tucked the boys into bed, poured myself a large glass of chardonnay and sat down on the couch with my laptop to open up a local internet dating site. As I scrolled the computer screen, a quirky looking man whose eyes darted in opposite directions caught my attention.

The next day I showed the man's online profile to a friend who told me she recognised this man as her neighbour. He was apparently a wealthy, world chess champion. She also recalled that he appeared to drag one of his legs as he walked and wore oversized floor-length raincoats. I began to question my decision to meet him but curiosity prevailed. Surely I could handle a quick picnic on the beach?

Despite wishing I could put appearances aside, his short stature, darting eyes and fashion choice of shorts, socks and sandals put me off my egg sandwiches.

Back home an email was already waiting.

'I like you a lot, Rebekah, and I want to know if you feel a romantic connection? If you do I would like to be intimate as soon as possible.

I know I am being direct but we are both adults.'

While I felt bad for the guy, I couldn't help my total lack of attraction.

'I am glad you have been direct,' I replied, 'because now I can be too. No, I do not feel a romantic connection. Full stop.'

I closed my laptop and walked over to clean my teeth before getting into bed. I looked at the yellow, pink and green post-it notes plastered over the bathroom mirror. W. C. Field's quote, 'If at first you don't succeed, try, try again,' caught my eye, so after putting on my pajamas I opened up my laptop again. Scrolling down the screen I saw another candidate named Jake. Noticing his eyes looked straight ahead I wasted no time in contacting him.

After a few email conversations I decided it was time to meet. A friend's wedding was coming up and sick of going to special events alone I asked Jake to come with me. It would be our first date. Jake and I were seated on a table with ten people I had never met before. I blushed when the man sitting opposite asked, 'How did you two meet?' The table went quiet.

'Internet dating,' Jake openly admitted.

I recoiled and took a large gulp of Champagne.

He had the five other couples' full attention.

'What kind of woman did you say you were looking for?' a guest asked.

'Young, sexy whore!' he said, uttering a huge roar of laughter.

Wine squirted out of my mouth.

I was not amused.

Neither was the rest of the table.

I didn't stay for the first dance, instead I went home and while standing in front of my bathroom mirror cleaning my teeth, I re-read W. C. Field's quote in its entirety: 'If at first you don't succeed, try, try again. Then quit. No use being a damn fool about it.'

Most of the time, I am happy as a single woman and am certainly not desperate to find a man. There was no male presence in my childhood and as Nanny lived a full life and truly flourished without a man, I was convinced it is possible to be content on one's own.

Besides, being single has its advantages. The freedom and independence I possess has allowed me to make my own choices in life, especially regarding my career and lifestyle. I am not answerable to anyone and, occasionally, when I long to have a partner, I believe I would never have ventured on our trip. What would a partner have answered when I said, 'Let's quit our jobs, sell our house and go?' Being single, the choice was mine.

I often wonder whether I've subconsciously chosen to remain single because I am not willing to compromise my lifestyle. Periodic remarks from friends such as, 'I thought I had trained my husband but every now and then he chews my shoes or pees on the couch,' sound a warning. After all, I have lived alone with my boys for the last eight years.

Although I appreciate this independence and freedom, a woman's need for love and intimacy cannot be completely fulfilled within the realms of motherhood and I still dream of having a lover.

All these desires passed through my mind as I continued to exchange glances with the intriguing stranger on the train a few rows away. Three hours elapsed and we still had not spoken. I could hardly leave the boys to chat up a stranger – could I? I tried to write in my journal but couldn't concentrate. I bought a cheese and ham sandwich and a bar of chocolate from the food cart, but wasn't able to eat. I spent most of the time trying to concoct a plan to introduce myself.

I decided I would discreetly make my move in the baggage collection area once we had reached our destination. Maybe I could strike up a conversation or slip him my phone number. I knew when the right moment came I'd know what to do, and then it would all work out perfectly from there. I imagined he was the man of my dreams, after all.

The train stopped and row-by-row the passengers disembarked. As he moved from his seat I was sweating with the excitement of a possible encounter.

I chose not to put on my unattractive yellow padded winter coat and stood shivering in the baggage area as the other passengers got off. I told Marco to keep an eye on his brother and the luggage, while I kept a sharp eye on the door.

'Mum, why are we waiting?' Marco asked.

'Um, we just need one more case to arrive,' I lied.

'No we don't. We have them all,' he argued.

Trust me to have such an efficient ten-year-old.

The baggage area was completely empty of passengers. Only the three of us remained. Like most men in my life, he was an illusion. I was devastated. Perhaps he was still nearby, waiting for a taxi or grabbing a coffee? I wanted to search the station for him, but that was impossible. So, I grabbed the boys and our cases and headed towards the metro. It was rush hour and people were pushing past me and shoving me out of the way. I wanted to scream with frustration. I felt so stupid. Like so many times before it had all been in my head. Or had it?

I tried to console myself. Perhaps he'd assumed that I was married, considering that I was travelling with two young boys. His lack of approach might have signalled the fact that he was a gentleman. Or maybe he just didn't fancy me.

Sometimes, I wish I could let fate take its course and believe if it was meant to happen it would have happened. Yet, in this case, like so many others, an inner voice had urged me on. I continued to believe that this story was not yet complete. Perhaps travelling with my boys was subconsciously driving me towards extremes of fantasy?

Whatever the reason, I decided this story was not going to end at Gare Central's baggage collection.

The frustration of being single for nearly eight years suddenly propelled me into becoming a woman on a mission. I was going to find the man from the train in case he was the man of my dreams. I just needed to work out how.

[Step 1] – **Profile:** The first step in this romantic pursuit was to generate a profile. His computer, grey suit and navy-blue tie made me presume that he was a commuter. If that was the case, the train journey from Quebec to Montreal was a regular one. Convinced I was correct, I decided I would meet the same train at the same time in the same place the following week. In preparation, I told Simone I wanted to go shopping in downtown Montreal and asked her to mind the boys. Next, I had to sort out what to wear. Even though the temperature was sub-zero, I was not going to wear layers. I chose a sexy black dress, tight fitting and cut just above the knee, and black heels; what any normal woman would wear on such an occasion. It worked for Marco's dad. Well, sort of.

At the train station I was overwhelmed by the freezing temperature. There was still thirty-five minutes to wait until the train from Quebec arrived. Commuters passing by stared at me in my flimsy attire as I glared back, envious of their warm coats. I tottered over to the platform and stood shivering in anticipation of my lover's arrival.

He never came.

Despondent? Yes. Surrender? No.

[Step 2] – **Research:** I scanned the employees working at the Information Bureau inside Gare Central, most were grouchy-looking men who seemed heartless and disinterested. I was about to give up when

I spotted Shirley through a long glass window. She had just sat down with a beaming smile and a red flower in her hair. Perfect. In that moment I knew she would help me find the man of my dreams.

I teetered over to her cubicle, trying to avoid my heels slipping on the melted ice and tugging at my dress to cover my frozen knees.

'Hello! My name is Rebekah,' I said smiling and holding out my hand.

'Hello Madam,' she replied, shaking my hand. 'Can I help you?'

'Yes please. I desperately need you to help me find love,' I answered, hoping that this introduction would make her an immediate ally. Before she had a chance to say no, I briefly described the situation and my desire to find this man from the train. I asked if she could contact him on my behalf, hoping that she would find his details in his booking file.

'Oh, I would love to help, but I really can't,' she replied. 'I'd get into serious trouble with my boss. It would be against our privacy policy.'

'Please, please, just this once,' I begged. 'I wont tell anyone you helped me. You don't have to give me his details. Just pass on mine and if he doesn't want to contact me after that, then I promise to accept that.'

In less than ten minutes Shirley was laughing, rubbing her hands at the prospect of assisting me. Her only request: she wanted an invite to the wedding if our plan succeeded.

Three cheers for sisterhood!

The first thing Shirley needed was the man's seat number so she could find his booking in the computer. Being uncertain of the number – in spite of having spent three hours staring at him – I suggested I needed to revisit the scene, sit in my original seat and try to recreate the moment of initial attraction. Without a flinch, Shirley ushered me through security and led me down to one of the trains waiting at the station. I should mention I had no ticket, showed no identification and could have been a professional stalker.

[Step 3] – Make the Call: After twenty minutes trying to visualise where the man had been sitting, I felt confident enough to give Shirley his seat number. With that information, Shirley said she would track down the man, ring him and, if she was able to get hold of him, give him my contact details. After that it would be up to him.

I lay awake that night, unable to sleep. Each time the phone rang I jumped up and grabbed the prompt cards I'd spent the afternoon writing in French. The phone was never for me. I began to worry that I had given Shirley the wrong number. By lunchtime the following day I was in despair, so I rang Shirley, but her colleague told me she was on leave for the next two days. I didn't know how I was going to wait that long, yet I had no choice.

She rang a few days later and informed me she had found the man and rung his office, but his grouchy secretary had refused to pass on my details. She told Shirley he worked in politics and was often bothered by irate citizens wanting to contact him. She couldn't take the risk that I might be one of them.

I was gutted. I had already begun planning our first date, our first holiday and the designer I'd call to make the wedding dress.

I tried comforting myself with the thought that maybe the universe was trying to tell me something. Perhaps I had to accept that this was not the man of my dreams, after all. Maybe it was time to give up.

[Step 4] – Do Not Give Up: Two weeks after returning to Canada from Doris's funeral in England, I was ready to leave again with Marco and Jack for new and exciting adventures in Europe when the phone rang. Marco answered it.

'Mum, it's for you,' Marco called.

'If it's the taxi company, tell them we need to be picked up at midday,' I yelled.

'It's not the taxi, Mum. It's some guy who says he's from the train. Some guy called Luc.'

I trembled in a state of panic. Days ago I would have had my script ready to recite on the phone. I was unprepared for this call. Furthermore, Jack was waiting for me to play Animal Snap after I finished packing the suitcases. He'd been begging me all morning. I knew in an instant I had to find a way of talking to Luc uninterrupted by a demanding toddler. I had to be quick. Then it came to me. I rapidly secured Jack into a highchair and furiously emptied a bag of thirty lollipops I had bought for the flight to London. It was a win-win situation – I talked to Luc on the phone for nearly an hour and Jack was in lollipop heaven.

When I returned to the phone I was elated though confused. How had Luc got my number? I understood his secretary had refused to pass on my message, but Shirley had rung Luc's workplace a second time, the day after she called me; this time his grumpy secretary was absent, giving Shirley the opportunity to speak to Luc directly. He told me he'd been flattered by Shirley's disclosure. Flattered, but also shocked and slightly cautious. He had never before encountered a woman so determined to track him down.

Since there was no way for us to meet before I left for Europe the following day, we decided to email each other over the next four months. If that went well, we'd catch up for a coffee on my return to Montreal in the summer. Luckily Luc couldn't see me in my flannelette pajamas, otherwise he may have not been so keen.

Afterwards, I sat dazed for a few moments. My detective skills and determination had paid off. For now, at least.

A few days later I received an email from Luc that included a song he had written about me called *Woman on a Train*. His lyrics – *like millions of stories arising from a gaze, just for a second on this round planet and rocking the world* – gave me goose bumps.

Could my desire to find love have begun?

PART 5

England

Chapter 7

I sat on a London bus with Marco beside me and Nanny on my lap. She was in a handcrafted box fashioned out of New Zealand kauri. My cousin Sarah was looking after Jack for the day.

I was on a pilgrimage to bury Nanny's ashes with my mother, in Saint Andrew's churchyard in Totteridge, London. In doing so, I was to fulfill Nanny's dying wish.

Bringing Nanny to England also provided me with the chance I'd been desperate for: to put Nanny first, to make her the centre of everything and to do it with love and tolerance. As a single mum, I had often lost patience with her. Juggling work, two young children, and a ninety-three-year-old grandmother meant I was forever exhausted. Each time I went to the washing machine and found more of Nanny's underwear inside waiting to be washed I would lose the plot. I was sick of having to pull them out so I could do my own washing. After repeatedly telling Nanny to put them in a bucket to soak, I yelled so loudly Nanny cried. When I saw this, instead of apologising, I called her a drama queen.

Thankfully, I eventually said sorry and Nanny laughed about my outbursts. Later, when I presented Nanny with a badge labelled 'Drama Queen', I was grateful we could joke together.

I wished Nanny and I had laughed together more often. There was never enough time. I was always trying to fit in chores like cooking her dinner, driving her to doctor's appointments and taking her on outings to give her some fresh air, in between rushing to school and kindergarten to pick up the boys. I thought that because Nanny was elderly and couldn't do a lot of these things by herself, she needed me. I did not realise until after her death how I had needed her more. The guilt of not acknowledging this until it was too late is something I will always live with, along with the shame of not having loved her enough. I am haunted by the image of her sitting alone on her couch, her frail body hunched over, as she waited for me to stop rushing around and sit down for a chat. I rarely did.

Nanny's mother, father, sisters Doris and Marjorie and brother Bill shared much laughter, love and happiness growing up together in London. However, Aunt Doris once told me that, as a young girl, Nanny would lock herself in the bathroom for hours plucking her eyebrows, curling her hair and grooming herself. Her father had to physically remove her so the rest of the family could use the one shared toilet.

Besides being vain, Nanny was also known as a flirt. In many early photographs she was surrounded by numerous adoring males. Doris said this was because she was beautiful. In fact, Nanny won the 'best legs in the office' award at one place of employment, a fact she loved to retell.

Nanny paid careful attention to her appearance even in her later years. At ninety-three she was proud she still had most of her own teeth and her nails were always impeccably manicured and painted fuchsia pink. Although she fretted when her hair became thinner, it did not deter her from combing it numerous times each day.

Nanny was not just my grandmother and mother – she was my best friend. She loved to travel and during her life we went to many exciting places together, particularly when I started working as a flight attendant for Air New Zealand at the age of twenty-two. I am certain that Nanny's adventurous character sparked my own desire to travel: Los Angeles, Norfolk Island, Sydney, Melbourne, London and Canada were just some of the destinations we visited together.

When Nanny was in her mid-seventies she came with me to Tijuana. There, we found a dimly-lit bar at midday, which had a revolving mirror-light shining and disco music blaring. The floor was sticky with spilt beer and men stood around smoking cheap cigars and getting drunk on tequila. This did not deter my nan from entering. In fact, when a couple of the bar flies started giving her the eye as she walked in wearing a turquoise silk blouse and orange flower-patterned skirt she took it in her stride. After one ice-cold Corona there was no holding her back, Nanny dragged me up in my denim shorts and red-and-white spotted blouse on the empty dance floor and we boogied the entire afternoon away.

During a trip to Melbourne to see *Phantom of the Opera*, Nanny and I queued outside the Princess Theatre in the rain along with hundreds of other hopefuls to get standby tickets. Five hours later, I wanted to give up and leave but Nanny pressed me to stay. Suddenly, it was our turn and we received the last tickets available.

Nanny was always keen to get out of the house. She was never one to sit at home crocheting, like some of my friends' grandmothers. At eighty-five she insisted on coming to the birth of my first son, Marco. I was happy for her to be with me during the early stages of my labour, but I had given Marco's dad Stephan strict instructions to keep her chair at the opposite end of the action. Although Nanny and I had a lifetime bond, the generation gap made me quiver at the thought of her seeing it all. However, as the day progressed and the contractions got closer so did her chair and when baby Marco emerged there stood Nanny holding a mirror for me to see the momentous occasion.

Nanny was ninety-two when I gave birth to Jack. Once again, she wanted to be there for the baby's arrival, but because Marco's labour was eighteen hours, I suggested she catch a taxi mid-morning, rather than come with Marco and me at five in the morning.

Unfortunately, Jack was in a hurry to be born and she didn't quite make it in time. When she did arrive she sat in the middle of the delivery suite while the doctor did some repairs. Just as the doctor picked up the needle to begin, Nanny produced a little bag of cheese and pickle sandwiches, which she proceeded to eat in neatly cut quarters. Then she asked if I was going to eat the food on my hospital tray, as she 'was famished.' Before I had a chance to reply she had grabbed my chicken roll. At least she took my mind off the stitches and for the first time in hours my face relaxed into a deep smile.

The last months of life took their toll on Nanny. Her once plump body had become a sack of skin and bones. Broken ribs and a shattered hip shortly followed a stroke. Suddenly, she was no longer the fighting spirit she had been – her face, her body, her words – everything indicated that she was ready to die, but I wasn't ready.

I was at working as a part-time teacher at the time, and preparing lessons when I heard from the rest home where Nanny was recuperating after her recent fall. It was eight-thirty in the morning and Nanny was struggling. The nurse inquired if I wanted her to remain at the rest home or to be taken to hospital.

'Take Nanny to the hospital, of course,' I snapped. 'And tell her I'll come and visit during my lunch hour.' *What was that stupid nurse thinking? How could she suggest leaving Nanny at the home? Why did she need to ask me? Wasn't it obvious? If Nanny was ill she needed a doctor.* I put down the phone and carried on with my day. Half an hour later the phone rang again.

'I'm sorry to tell you your nan is not going to make it to the hospital.'

I dropped the phone. Nanny had always recovered from strokes, broken hips and multiple broken ribs. I couldn't believe that this time she might not.

I drove as fast as I could in heavy rain. Traffic was stationary and my eyes were bleary and stinging with tears.

Nanny lay in a room alone.

The nurse told me her last words had been, 'I want to sit next to Rachel.'

Who the hell was Rachel?

Then I understood.

All my life people have confused the names Rachel and Rebekah. She wasn't asking for Rachel.

Nanny was dying and calling for me.

I wasn't there.

Instead she was alone.

How could I have deserted her?

Why didn't I leave work when I received the first call?

How could I have let her down so badly after everything she had done for me?

Five bloody minutes late.

I should have been prepared for Nanny's death when it finally happened. After all, I had been waiting for her to die for nearly thirty years.

Growing up I was certain that every ambulance rushing past was heading for my house to take Nanny away. She was old compared with my friends' mothers. When I was twelve and my friend Fiona came over for sleepovers she would spend half the night comforting me after I'd woken her convulsed in a fit of fear over losing Nanny. I was terrified of what might happen when she died and if I was left all alone in the world.

Becoming a mother changed my attitude and what she meant to me. Nanny was the only other person who interacted with my boys on a daily basis. Every day, Marco and Jack would run for a morning hug and at night she would ask them to come to her room so that she could kiss them goodnight. She made us a family.

Before she died she would wait up through the night whenever I took one of the boys to the hospital with a fever or rash. I would often be irritated by her insistence on keeping her informed, even when there was nothing to report.

Nanny's anxiety about my wellbeing was not new. It occurred much earlier, long before the boys were born. I returned home one evening from a movie with a male suitor when my neighbour Lorraine phoned, she had been frantically trying to reach me after receiving a call from Nanny. Apparently, Nanny had just telephoned Lorraine to say she was about to ring the police because she had heard footsteps and suspected intruders were in my part of the house. I rang Nanny, who lived downstairs in the granny flat and furiously notified her that the footsteps she could hear were mine. I was now purple with rage and humiliation as I returned to the good-looking doctor, but he now had his coat on and was walking out the door.

Now Nanny had died, I deeply regretted my dismissive attitude concerning her watchfulness. Everyone needs a soft place to fall and now my safety net had gone. No longer would there be someone waiting up when I took sick boys to the hospital or came home with a new man. I envy my friends whose mothers are still here to care about them and their children, as only a mother, a grandmother or a great-grandmother can do.

The bus pulled up outside the church in Totteridge. Marco, Nanny and I disembarked. We had forgotten to bring flowers, so Marco picked a few daffodils from a nearby garden. The service was simple with only the vicar and my mother's cousin Elizabeth present. I smiled as Nanny's ashes were buried alongside my mother.

After the service, Elizabeth took Marco for a walk so I could sit and chat with my mum and Nanny, the three of us together for the first time in thirty-six years. Two wood pigeons sang in the sunshine. I took off my coat and lay it on the grass to sit beside the tombstone. I ran my hands over the engraving of my mother's name, Alison, and looked at the blank space that would soon be engraved with the words:

MARGARET AMY TYLER (PEGGY),
1913–2006.
A loving mum, nanny,
great-nana & sister.
Love you forever.

The stone felt smooth and cold, yet my heart was warm. I told Mummy and Nanny my concerns about raising the boys alone and wondered if I was going to be as strong as the two of them had been.

Since I had their attention, I couldn't help myself and had to tell them about Luc. In the past, Nanny had sat through many hours of similar stories and I am sure my mother would have wanted to hear too. I pulled out Luc's latest email and read it quietly beside the grave.

I told them how happy I was that Luc admired and was impressed by my 'perseverance' to track him down. I loved that he also recognised my 'bravery' for travelling the world with the boys. My kind of man. When I finished I waited for some kind of sign from Nanny and Mum to say they approved. There was only silence. I think it was the approving kind.

I returned the email back into my backpack and pulled out a bag of cheese and pickle sandwiches, bit into the fresh white bread, and began the next chapter of my life.

Chapter 8

'I'm not going any further!' Marco yelled as he threw himself down in the mud. An elderly man on the other side of the path noticed the commotion and walked over. He introduced himself as Ted.

'What's going on here?' he asked, smiling kindly at my angry son. I explained that while trying to keep within my budget, I refused to pay for a taxi to drive us to our accommodation. Instead we had taken a bus that dropped us off at the top of a long winding road. I had assumed the road would gently lead down to the guesthouse where we were staying.

I was wrong.

Marco had spent twenty minutes lugging two suitcases and three backpacks down dirt roads and through dense forest in the rain while I pushed Jack in the pushchair with my right hand and carted the other bags with my left. At the end of the forest we came to a muddy path. That was when Marco decided that enough was enough and collapsed in tears.

Ted sympathetically offered to drive us to our accommodation, but this created a dilemma as I knew we couldn't all fit into his car along with our luggage. I then suggested Ted might take just Marco and our baggage. I would carry on alone, pushing Jack in his stroller.

I know that handing over my son to a complete stranger might seem risky, but spending most of my parenting years as a single mum

I have come to rely on the generosity of strangers. In doing so, I have developed intuition about whom I can trust and I want to teach the boys to do the same. Besides, I needed help. Marco wasn't going any further on foot.

Nonetheless, I made sure Jack was strapped securely in his stroller and ran as fast as I could after the car, a tightness growing in my chest. When I saw Marco waiting on the doorstep surrounded by our luggage I ran up and hugged him so tightly he couldn't breathe.

The Isle of Wight was the place my great-aunt Doris and Nanny brought me for the summer holidays during my childhood until Nanny and I moved to New Zealand. I can still feel my legs shaking as I stood on stage at the Ventnor Hall, aged four, singing *Miss Polly had a Dolly*. The venue attracted hundreds of holidaymakers like us to its weekly talent show. We stayed in a little house on the beach in the village of Bonchurch. Charles Dickens once described this place as, 'the prettiest place I ever saw in my life...' It was here on the Isle of Wight that Dickens had found the inspiration to write *David Copperfield*. I worried that this quaint village I had visited during my childhood might have changed. However, on the way to our guesthouse we passed the same village pond that thirty years ago I had stood next to for hours, throwing small pieces of stale white bread to the ducks. We also walked by the same pebble beach where I had met John, another eight-year-old who had come there on holiday from the mainland. The two of us had met each morning to construct forts with the pebbles and pieces of driftwood which had swept onto the shore. It was as if time had stood still here in the Isle of Wight.

We stayed for eight days at Horseshoe Bay Guest House, a two-storey stone house that had been converted into a luxurious bed and breakfast. Each white shuttered window looked out over the Atlantic Ocean. The view was more breathtaking than the travel book had promised, so when a terrible storm forced us to stay indoors for the first two days we did so happily. Warm and relaxed in our airy, spacious room, we watched the fury of the waves pounding against the rocks.

At first the boys' faces had been glued to the windows, fascinated by the wild ocean. When the novelty of this wore off we began a Scrabble tournament – not an easy task with a two-year-old trying to eat the letters. As we know, boys need to move and a room measuring ten feet by fifteen feet – regardless of the view – just doesn't compensate.

In desperation, I decided it would be fun to stroll along the seafront to the neighbouring village of Ventnor and grab some lunch at the Spyglass Inn, a family-run pub situated on the waterfront. However, the storm had increased and flood warnings were issued across England. Rain and gale-force winds travelling at 80 mph effected road, rail and air travel and almost 12,000 homes across the country were without power. The proprietor, Christine, tried to talk me out of going for a walk, warning of the danger of being swept into the sea, but I would not be deterred. We put on our waterproof coats and gumboots, I strapped Jack securely into his pushchair and we waved farewell to Christine, who stood shaking her head.

I soon realised I should have listened when the waves crashed onto the shore with such force we had to cower behind a feeble metal railing, holding onto it to prevent being swept out to sea. By the time we returned we were drenched. The boys squealed with delight, but my knuckles and face had turned ghostly white and I firmly decided thereafter we'd continue playing Scrabble in our room until the storm subsided.

What truly made Horseshoe Bay Guest House so unique and rewarding were its proprietors Christine and Howard. Howard was away in Austria skiing during the first six days of our visit, but we did get to know Christine quite intimately.

From the time of our arrival, she quickly became involved in our lives, doing our washing everyday, driving us around the island sightseeing after the storm had subsided and playing Scrabble with us. She also looked after the boys so I could visit the local internet café to respond to Luc's latest emails.

On the first occasion I ran back in pouring rain to tell Christine how excited I was after reading Luc's words, 'I just received your photo a few minutes ago. I confirm you really are this pretty woman of the train with incredible eyes and smile. No doubt now. I remember very well when our eyes met.'

Luc's compliment made me feel special and kept replaying in my mind as I ran through the rain back home.

I looked in the mirror behind Christine and caught sight of my reflection: rain-sodden hair was plastered against my face and mascara ran down my cheeks and yet I didn't care. I felt gorgeous.

Christine eagerly volunteered to babysit and cook dinner for Jack some evenings so Marco and I could eat out at restaurants without the tantrums of an exhausted two-year-old. The offer came after Christine received a report from her sister Carol that Jack had caused havoc during a visit to the Lake Hotel's restaurant, owned by Carol and her husband, Richard. Ordinarily this establishment refused entry to children under the age of eight to keep the ambience quiet and romantic. However, Christine persuaded her relatives to make an exception so that we could dine in the hotel's restaurant and enjoy a five-course meal including wine for a mere twelve pounds, an absolute bargain by British standards.

During our first visit my feeling of anticipation turned to dread as we entered the hushed dining room full of middle-aged couples, sitting upright, dressed immaculately, whispering and reading newspapers and books. When the boys ran into the room laughing, the patrons turned and stared as if each boy had two heads and ten arms.

We tried to sit down without causing too much disturbance. This might have been possible if it had not been for the waitress who left a basket of bread and crackers on our table. Immediately we ate the soft buttery bread, enjoying our first dinner out together since we'd left Canada, but before we'd had time for a second piece, the waitress whipped the basket away half eaten, only to pass it on to the next table. Jack revolted and, with high-pitched squeals, shouted, 'I want more bread!' One female guest in a pale lilac twinset and pearls glared his way and ordered him to 'Shush.' Unfortunately, this incited Jack further and as he sat in front of a hot bowl of soup while holding a sharp knife in his left hand I froze waiting to see which item would be flung first. Luckily, neither was thrown but after gobbling down our roast beef dinner, I dragged Jack out.

My decision to travel the world with the boys often placed Jack in difficult adult situations. A two-year-old probably needs a strict routine as part of his early childhood development, so it wasn't easy. By this stage of our trip he had already slept in seven different beds (the number would increase to twenty-five by the end of our trip), which is testimony to his sense of resilience and his inherited love of new experiences.

Regardless of Jack's ability to adapt to his surroundings, sitting quietly in elegant restaurants was a different matter, so Christine insisted that Marco and I go out without Jack for a quiet meal to have some mother-son time. Christine's support, like Auntie Dan's and Uncle Francois' in Canada, was a welcome reprieve from the life I led in New Zealand, where I had little relief. Quality time back home was lacking and most days, marred by exhaustion on all sides, especially by dinner time, I'd sit down at the table and shout, 'Jack, stop eating with food in your mouth!'

One evening Marco had persistently told me little events that had occurred during his day: how many marble games he had won at lunch, the number of basic facts he had answered correctly and the different middle names of all the boys in his class. Ten minutes of this became irritating.

'Marco, please give me five minutes of quiet. I'm exhausted. I just want to eat my dinner.'

Marco couldn't restrain himself. Shortly after he started to recite the thirty-five ingredients on the tomato ketchup bottle that sat on the table.

'Shuuuuuuuuut uuuuuuuuuuuuup!' I screamed.

And so with the support of Christine, Marco and I were able to make a second visit to the Lake Hotel's restaurant, without the worry of Jack. I hoped that Marco and I might have an uninterrupted conversation and maybe even eat our food while it was still hot.

During our dessert of apple crumble Marco asked, 'Why are all those men and ladies not talking to each other?' Scanning the room, I noticed one woman sat stiffly in her chair, watching her husband read *The Times* newspaper. She fiddled with her pearl necklace and shifted her glass of sherry backwards and forwards across the table. She opened her mouth and a small bird-like sound came out. It was muffled by the rustling noise of the paper as her husband turned the pages. He hadn't noticed, yet her eyes were fixed on him. The lack of conversation made me wonder how many of these middle-aged wives were leading frustrated and unsatisfied lives. Did any of them dream of leaving their family homes and marital responsibilities to travel the world?

Eight glorious days and nights later at Horseshoe Bay Guest House we waved goodbye to Christine, who stood blowing kisses to us on the dock long after the ferry had departed for England's south coast. We'd had such a relaxing stay with Christine, I never thought unpleasant times would be awaiting us at our next destination.

Bath #1: Next stop was supposedly a three-night luxury stay at Florence House, an Edwardian boutique hotel in Portsmouth. A 'luxury spa bath' was the enticement, which I knew the boys and I would enjoy.

When we returned to the hotel with our feet covered in blisters after our first day visiting the town's historic dockyard, I filled the bath with hot water and turned on the powerful jets. I went to the minibar and poured a cold glass of chardonnay to sip in the bath.

I was horrified to see a rush of black mould gushing into the tub. I gulped to keep down my lunch. I phoned the owner and tried to remain calm when he casually told me not to use the spa, promising his cleaners would fix the problem the next day. This was an establishment described as being, 'all about class.'

Next evening, after another long day on our feet, we all looked forward to the spa, but when we tried the faucet, black fragments of filth invaded us again. This time I refused to 'stay calm' and insisted that the owner visit the room and see the foul sight for himself. When he was unable to remedy the issue, I informed him we would be leaving his filthy-bath establishment two days early.

I have never received the refund the proprietor promised, but take comfort in the hope he will get his just deserts one day – in the form of problems with his own plumbing!

Bath #2: Leaving this unsavoury place behind we took the train to the south coast village of Osmington. I had booked two weeks at Laurel Cottage, a stone house with a thatched roof accommodating up to four people. Luckily, the owner allowed us to move in two days early.

An invigorating wind greeted us at Weymouth Beach, where Jack enjoyed a donkey ride and Marco delighted in the funfair attractions. The wind had chilled us to the bone so I promised to run the boys a soothing, hot bath and then prepare dinner for them. When the water reached the halfway mark in the tub the hot water ran cold and the boys shivered in their meager lukewarm bath before jumping out covered in goose bumps. I hoped the water would reheat, but it didn't. My plan for a relaxing hot soak, glass of wine and the last few pages of *Love Junkie* turned into a hurried wash in a few inches of tepid water.

Next morning I rang the owner to complain, but like the Portsmouth proprietor, he took no responsibility and offered no help. Instead, he haughtily told me to either share a bath or take a shower. I argued that since I was paying hundreds of pounds for the week I should be entitled to my own full, hot bath. He didn't give a damn and simply hung up.

I don't know why I expected a decent plumbing experience in England. It's not as though the situation had been all that different when I stormed out of my grandfather's home aged seventeen, when a generous East London family invited me to stay. The family collected reptiles. Every time I took a bath (there was no shower) I had to remove four water terrapins, place them in a bucket of water and wash the slimy bath before I stepped in. When I was finished I then had to fill the bath with cold water and replace the squirming creatures. Although this family made me feel more welcome than my grandfather ever had, when they announced they were getting a boa constrictor I realised I had swapped one reptile for another and did another runner.

After six more nights of unsatisfactory baths in Laurel Cottage I knew exactly what I needed to do. I rang Christine and asked her if we could return to the Isle of Wight. She seemed slightly surprised, but when I heard her call out to Howard, 'Pull three more steaks out of the freezer! Our Kiwi family are coming for dinner,' I knew that it was worth cutting our Osmington stay in half and forfeiting hundreds of pounds.

As Christine and Howard stood on the dock waiting for us with open arms, I knew that travelling the world was also about finding family among strangers.

Chapter 9

Being a single mum means it's up to me – alone – to discover suit-able activities for my boys. I do my best, but there is a limit to all the swimming competitions, robotic tournaments, chess tournaments, basketball games, cricket games, rugby tournaments and football matches I can handle. Yet, when I replay film footage of the boys' football games all I can hear is my voice screaming 'go faster,' 'tackle' and 'awesome!' You would never guess I'd been shivering on the sideline in the pouring rain with numb toes. Growing up without a mother has made me determined to be the best mum I can be, regard-less of the weather. As you can imagine this has not always been easy when the repetition of kids' activities eventually becomes boring.

New adventures presented themselves when we reached London. In five days we made every moment count, despite Jack tugging on one arm and Marco lagging behind.

The highlight for Jack and me was the performance of *The Lion King* at Covent Garden's Lyceum Theatre.

Initially I was concerned that Jack, being two years old, would find the three-hour performance too long. Moreover, I was nervous that he would be refused entry. In spite of this, Jack's obsession with music drove me to take the risk. What a fabulous time he had. He hadn't stopped for one minute – for three straight hours, he provided accom-paniment to the orchestra with his air guitar, flute, piano and drums.

For my part, the opening scene and its song, *Circle of Life*, which had played at Nanny's funeral, triggered immediate tears.

Marco shook his head and tried to detach himself from the two of us.

Immersing the boys in culture like the theatrical performance of *The Lion King* helped to ease any guilt I was feeling about Marco's lack of schooling. When Stephan had raised concerns before our departure about Marco's absence from school for eight months, I argued that my skills as a newly-trained primary teacher would prevent him getting behind.

Before we left I planned daily lessons in math and writing, but our escapades soon took preference. However, when Marco spelled the words 'excavation' and 'parched' during a game of Scrabble I said, 'Marco, you are using a lot of big words at the moment.'

'Yes,' he replied proudly, 'I think I am getting puberty early.'

I just smiled not wanting to disappoint him.

Other than mastering the correct definition of puberty, I believe that Marco's improved language skills were a result of the many stimulating conversations about travel, history, different cultures, art and politics that he had with adults we met. I know these strangers also benefited from their interaction with Marco. He was always keen to talk about technology, especially the functions on their cameras and phones, a subject he was passionate about. One elderly woman in London now has the sound of gunshots on her phone as a text message alert. I bet the oldies at her bingo hall are wishing they'd met Marco, too.

Knowing Marco needed to learn subjects other that technology inspired us to visit London's Natural History Museum where Marco could 'come face-to-face with stunning specimens, historic characters, live animals and Museum scientists.' It was also a safe place for Jack to run around and let off steam. So on our last day in England, we spent three hours darting from dinosaurs to blue whales to volcanoes in the huge building that housed over seventy million exhibits.

Running around the museum all morning left us starving, so we trudged to Harrods department store to buy lunch. En route, Marco wanted us to stop.

'Please Mum, look at this wall,' he pleaded as he pointed to something on a wall.

Desperate for lunch I reluctantly stopped with Jack, who was fast asleep in his pushchair. I noticed Marco was running his hand over small holes, scattered in the concrete wall.

'Read this, Mum,' he said steering me to a small plaque commemorating the impact of German bombs which struck the wall during World War II. My desire to satisfy my hunger had almost denied Marco and myself the opportunity to witness the result of such a historical event.

We stood there quietly, imagining the terrified men, women and children who would have been scurrying past this very place years ago.

Better than a classroom.

I was excited taking Marco and Jack to Harrods' sumptuous food hall. Nanny had taken me there as a child during our annual visits to central London from our flat in Barnet to view the Christmas lights on Regent Street.

We were not disappointed. Marco, like me, has always been obsessed with food, which made me keen to introduce him to this gourmand's delight. We rushed to the bakery to buy fresh jam doughnuts, the same delicious treat that Nanny had bought me. The sugary smell and warm, soft texture tempted us to eat them immediately. They tasted even better than they had thirty-five years ago.

Just as I was about to eat the second doughnut I felt a tap on my shoulder. Suddenly, I found myself face to face with a scowling security guard, who escorted us outside with a stern reprimand.

'No food is to be consumed on the premises, Madam.'

My face turned red and I cringed as we walked past our fellow customers who stood sneering at us for not following the rules. This was certainly unlike our food market back home where I ate from the trolley as we shopped the aisles.

Outside on the pavement we finished our buns before returning, feeling like outcasts, though I still maintain those piping hot doughnuts that melted in our mouths were well worth the embarrassment.

With sugary faces, we walked from the bakery to the deli section and bought Indian tandoori chicken for a picnic in nearby Hyde Park. Cars, taxis and buses whizzed past us with horns blaring as we walked through London's concrete jungle and stern-looking commuters hurried by, dodging Jack as he skipped from left to right. In Hyde Park it was wonderful to be among acres of greenery, filled with the sounds of children playing and blackbirds singing. We sat in the warm sun and enjoyed a moment of solitude as we ate our delicious spicy tandoori with only a few pigeons for company.

After lunch we discovered Diana, Princess of Wales' Memorial Playground on the other side of Hyde Park in Kensington Gardens. I was surprised to find we had to press a button on a locked gate to gain entry. I assumed this kept children from escaping and getting lost in the vast park.

Even though Marco and Jack spent two hours running and climbing the park's Peter Pan sculptures and pirate ship, when time ran out I had to drag them away. As soon as the gate closed Marco said, 'Mum, you've left Jack's pushchair behind.'

When I pressed the button on the gate to go back inside I was denied entry. A woman's harsh voice came through a speaker saying, 'Sorry, Madam, but you cannot enter without a child.' It then dawned on me the secured gate was not to stop children leaving but to prohibit potential pedophiles from entering.

The locked gate mentality was in contrast to New Zealand, where children were still free to explore the environment on their own. I was starting to think that my life with the boys back home wasn't so bad after all.

As we boarded the Eurostar at St Pancras station I wondered how France would be. Would it be more or less edgy than London? And would it be as hectic?

Collapsing into my seat for the two-and-a-half-hour train trip to Paris I reflected on our time in London. In just three days we had visited the London Aquarium, the London Eye, taken The Original London Bus Tour, toured the Natural History Museum, Harrods, Hyde Park, Kensington Gardens, Hamleys Toy Shop, Trafalgar Square, seen *The Lion King* and stood beneath Big Ben as it chimed midday. All of this was accomplished in a city of over seven million with two young boys in tow. Long queues and a sea of foot traffic frequently confronted us, but this was London, so we did what any Londoner would do – we walked with purpose and shoved ourselves to the front.

Shortly after the train departed I spread out the souvenir brochures of all the places we had visited and asked Marco which of these attractions had been his favourite. He studied them for many minutes. I waited, certain he was going to say The Natural History Museum, since he had always had a huge interest in dinosaurs and often had to be persuaded not to read the fine print of every single exhibit. He finally replied, 'I really liked the local sweet shop, but I can't decide whether my favourite sweets were the pear drops or the wine gums.'

Great! I'd given up my job, sold our house and travelled thousands of miles so Marco could enjoy wine gums!

PART 6

France

Chapter 10

Back home in Devonport, apart from the occasional foreign film, I grab a little fantasy through my daily visits to a local French delicatessen, Chateaubriant. I speak a little French to the tall, dark-haired shopkeepers when I order my *pain au chocolat*, croissants and coffee. In my kitchen I hang a string of onions to make French onion soup in true French tradition.

Yet, this hasn't been enough. For the last ten years I have longed to revisit cities like Paris and Rome, as I did before I had children. Since then my only escape from the routine of everyday life has been through films and imagination. A movie might transport me from Devonport, New Zealand to the streets of Prague, New York or Mexico. I was able to escape momentarily and leave behind the mundane aspects of life. I could find myself identifying with the characters as they ambled along dark cobblestone streets, stopping to embrace and kiss. I became immersed in their love affairs. When the lights came on I quickly used my sleeve to wipe away the tears. I may have felt heartbroken at the end of *Betty Blue*, but at least I was able to feel. For a woman who's been single for many years, this stirring of emotion filled me with wonder and hope that I too might experience adventure and romance one day.

Many of my married friends have argued that I have the best of both worlds. I get my 'love fix' through cinema, after which I snuggle into my warm flannelette sheets without a sweaty, snoring partner who steals the covers. When I feel the need again for intoxicating romance, all I have to do is hand over twelve dollars and have another chance to fall in love.

My desire to escape into a world of fantasy led to the decision to begin a Film and Media Studies degree when Marco was two. On the first day of classes I dropped Marco off at the university crèche and went to my first lecture. My dream was to be a film critic, imagining I could be paid to watch movies all day. We began with the theory of film and I felt overwhelmed as I took my seat in the large, packed lecture theatre. When the lecturer appeared I furiously scribbled notes for the next fifty minutes, trying to impress the other students and the lecturer and prove I had some understanding of his academic jargon. I wondered if the younger students felt as nervous as I did.

If I felt out of my depth, at least I looked stylish sitting in class wearing a black cat suit, knee-high boots and a black patent raincoat, as if I had just stepped off the set of *The Avengers*. I was a woman who wanted to let those around me know I didn't want ordinary. I didn't want to be labelled; be it mother, single mother or woman from suburbia. Sitting in class in my sexy ensemble I felt my life had the potential to become just as exciting as any film I was studying.

Our visit to Paris started in the one-bedroom apartment of my friend Isabelle, whom I had met in Africa eleven years earlier when I lived there for a short time after marrying Stephan. Stephan and I were regulars at the beachfront restaurant in the small village of Grand Popo where Isabelle worked as a waitress. Life was relaxed back then. Wine flowed and laughter and conversation were uninterrupted. I was excited to see Isabelle again after such a long time, but I was also a little nervous. She had no children and her life was the same.

Mine had changed dramatically.

As soon as we arrived with all our luggage, Isabelle, who was smoking a Camel cigarette declared, 'We don't eat until nine p.m., I'll be chatting on internet sites until three a.m. and I don't get up until at least eleven a.m. each day, so please keep the boys quiet.' How was I going to make the boys tiptoe around Isabelle, who was sleeping on the couch? To make matters worse, yet again there was no hot water. Isabelle's plumbing was broken. When the boys asked for a bath, I had to boil water and fifteen kettles later the cold, steel bath was still only one-quarter full. Marco and Jack sat shivering, calling out for more water. I ignored their pleas and collapsed exhausted onto the couch with Isabelle and two full glasses of pinot noir.

On the first night I had to fight for space in the double bed I shared with both Marco and Jack. Although this was only our first day it had not begun well, and bore no resemblance to Gene Kelly's bright and magical *An American in Paris*. When I woke I recalled the words of lead character, Lise Bouvier, 'Maybe Paris has a way of making people forget.' Trying to move my aching body that was riddled with pins and needles after enduring five inches of bed space, I hoped her words might come true.

On the other hand, I was very appreciative that Isabelle hadn't reprimanded Jack when he took all the books off her shelf to build a tower in the middle of the extremely small kitchen. Nor had she frowned at the ten pieces of luggage now blocking her hallway, so much so that to get to the kitchen she had to slide with her back against the wall trying not to knock her family photos off the wall.

However, even after this short time, I couldn't imagine a two-year-old, ten-year-old, chain-smoking Isabelle and me together in her miniscule *pied-à-terre* for two weeks. I tossed and turned during the night, so when morning came I had already firmly decided we would move to a hotel in central Paris. I already longed for a place where I could soak in a hot bubble bath, sleep in a bed without eight thrashing limbs and breathe easily in a smoke-free environment. I woke

Isabelle at eleven o'clock and using the excuse that her apartment was too far from the main tourist sights said, 'Sorry, Isabelle, but the boys and I have decided to move to a hotel in the centre of town.'

'Oh that's a shame,' Isabelle replied with a slight smile as she sat nursing her foot after standing on a sharp piece of Jack's Lego.

When Isabelle left for work I searched the internet for a listing of local hotels and began to make my calls. The first nineteen were fully booked. I began to panic. How could I call Isabelle and tell her I'd changed my mind? I should have made the booking before telling her we were leaving.

Two hours later, I secured a reservation at the Minerve Hotel. Situated in the heart of the Latin Quarter, the hotel had rooms with wrought-iron balconies that looked out over the tree-laden Rue des Ecoles, busy with pedestrians hurrying past or stopping at one of the many cafes, bookstores or *pâtisseries* that lined the street. Okay, so it was going to cost me an arm and a leg but I didn't care. This was the Paris I dreamed of. Besides, the Minerve's location, only a stone's throw from the Notre Dame, meant we could walk to most attractions or use the nearby metro. Being in the heart of all the excitement of Paris was worth every euro.

Lying on the hotel bed that evening, I realised how our arrival in Paris at Isabelle's had not quite begun as planned. Now we had no family or friends to look after us, as we had enjoyed in England and Canada. We were now in unfamiliar territory. There was nobody to show us around, cook our meals or do our washing. The only thing I had to rely on was a Lonely Planet guidebook. Our *real* adventure was about to begin with no one to help us if we ran into trouble. I finally realised this was what I had left New Zealand to experience and I couldn't wait.

The adventure began as soon as we stepped out of our hotel the next morning. Paris was swamped with police cars speeding past with sirens blaring. Heavily armed *gendarmes* and riot police lined the streets to keep order. A protest of China's treatment of Tibet had been planned to coincide with the running of the 2008 Olympic flame through Paris. However, we never actually saw any confrontation, instead the *gendarmes* seemed to spend much of their time greeting each other with hugs and kisses while they hung around waiting for something to happen.

Jack wanted to stay and watch the police action, but I was wooed by the smell of warm baguettes, butter-roasted chickens and freshly brewed coffee. The Minerve Hotel was surrounded by eateries. We soon became familiar with places like the local Greek deli, which served the creamiest tzatziki, which we spread onto warm slices of crusty baguette. It took only two visits before Andreas, the owner, welcomed us by name and always had time for a chat. This warm hospitality made us feel accepted by the neighbourhood. A sense of belonging, even in a strange land, was comforting.

Another restaurant we returned to frequently was Chartier. At first I felt I had just walked onto the set of *A Long Engagement*, an Audrey Tautou film set in Paris during World War I.

Chartier was situated on Rue du Faubourg in Montmartre and from the photographs on the wall, looked virtually the same as it did when it first opened in 1896. There were wooden racks above each table, where I placed my coat and bag, and numbered drawers were next to each section of tables, where regular customers had originally kept their personal linen. Chartier still provided daily dinners for over 300 patrons, which made it difficult to hear the boys' demands for more dessert above the clamour of crockery and chatter. At least my boys' noise didn't offend anyone for a change.

An exception occurred when Marco tried cutting into his prof-iterole, which was unexpectedly frozen. It flew like a rocket into the air, just missing the eye of an elderly woman.

Shrinking in my seat, I smiled with relief that this incident had not been witnessed by any of the waiters, who rushed around in their *rondin* (traditional black waistcoat and long white apron), hurriedly writing down guests' orders on the white paper tablecloths. They were mostly elderly gentlemen who scowled each time Marco or Jack asked for more water. However, Chartier's eight and a half euro *Steak hache au poivre vert et frites* more than made up for the waiters' disapproval.

Another of our favourite restaurants in the same area was La Maison Rose. It was just around the corner from the famous Roman Catholic church, Sacré Coeur, which we visited many times. I found La Maison Rose in the same way I found Chartier – through the *Lonely Planet Guide*. Wherever we went on our adventures in Europe I was never disappointed with the guidebook's recommendations.

La Maison Rose was a little bistro named after its pink paintwork. It offered outdoor seating where we could eat three-course lunches for sixteen euros whilst watching the locals walk past. On our first four visits I ordered the same *carte du jour: la soupe à l'oignon, poulet à l'estragon* and the most incredible melt-in-your-mouth *crème brûlée*. I wanted to try something new, so each time I spent fifteen minutes or so reading through the menu.

'Mum, just order your normal chicken,' Marco would say after about ten minutes. He knew me too well.

On our fifth visit I decided to be adventurous. Marco almost choked on his lemonade when I suggested that we try snails for the first time – we were in France after all. After ordering, Marco and I spent a long time staring at them, while Jack gobbled his half-dozen down. Marco and I managed to eat one snail each, quickly washed down with a glassful of water. I felt sick, so I waved my arm at the waiter and ordered a double portion of *crème brûlée* to get rid of the taste, while Jack demanded I order him a second plate of snails.

After the *crème brûlée* Marco asked if we could go up to the top of the Sacré Coeur.

'Yes,' I replied. 'But first, I want to take you and Jack to look for a street artist in Montmartre. I want to have portraits drawn of you both to hang on our wall back home.'

I had seen examples of these when I was seven years old and visiting my older cousins' house in Windsor, England. I stood admiring the oil portraits of Sarah and Caroline that hung on the wall.

'Where did you get those pretty paintings from?' I asked.

'Mummy and Daddy had an artist paint them when we went on holiday to Paris a few summers ago,' Sarah replied.

Two years later, when I was getting ready for my cousin Sarah's wedding, I took off my dungarees and sneakers and put on the yellow cotton dress that Nanny had made for me. I tied back my short bob as best I could and placed a pink daisy behind my ear.

'Look Nanny,' I said as I twirled around the room. 'This dress would be perfect for a portrait like the one of Sarah when she was nine like me.'

'Sorry, Rebekah,' she replied. 'We just can't afford it at the moment.' The moment never came.

So after paying the bill at La Maison Rose, Marco, and I wove our way through the narrow cobblestone streets with Jack firmly secured in the pushchair, in search of an artist. Suddenly the sound of a guitar distracted us. An Italian-accented version of U2's *One Love* lured us to the base of the Sacré Coeur. A dark-haired Italian had a large crowd of enthusiastic tourists swaying, singing and clapping. What fun it was to lounge on the steps of the Sacré Coeur, surrounded by the energy of youth, sunshine warming our faces and music.

After some time, I reluctantly pulled the boys away from the revelry to continue my search for an artist, but not before buying Youri's CD.

As we walked around Place du Tertre, we passed many illustrators eyeing us for work. I was looking for someone special and I knew I would know once I'd found the right person. I was attracted to the work of a broad-shouldered man, wearing baggy white trousers and a red-and-orange checked shirt. Unlike many of the other artists, who used black-and-white pastels, he painted in rich, vibrant colour. His bearded face and kind eyes drew me to him. So, when I saw another family approaching his stand, I quickly grabbed Jack's hand and cut them off.

'*Madame*, I was a graduate from the famous École des Beaux-Arts school and I have been creating portraits here for over twenty years.'

Twenty years? Really? I was a little skeptical. 'Twenty years' experience' sounded like a sales pitch meant to reel in tourists like me. Yet when an American family arrived shortly after I was proven wrong. Delighted with the man's sketches of their two grown-up children drawn fifteen years ago, this couple had returned with their two newly adopted children for portraits.

Remarkably, Jack sat still for nearly an hour while the artist worked his pastel magic. Jack's patience was due to the artist's colleague Jacque, who spent fifty minutes making origami animals, transfixing Jack, and keeping him still as the artist worked. Seeing the pastel image of Jack's face and then Marco's appear on the blank paper made my eyes well up. My walls back home would finally have family portraits hung on them.

'And now,' said Jacque after handing Jack a paper lion, 'I will make a heart for your *maman*.' Ten minutes later, I accepted the red paper heart, smiled and went to slip it into my handbag.

'Sorry *Madame*, but the heart will cost you five euros.'

When I refused to pay, on the grounds that I hadn't asked him to make it for me, the heart was withheld. Story of my life!

As soon as the portraits were finished Jack and Marco needed to run. There was no better place for this than the 234 spiraling stairs to the dome of the Sacré Coeur. After we raced each other to the top I was overwhelmed by the view of Paris spread out below in the setting sun. It was a vista I had seen many times before on film and always a scene that on screen conjured up feelings of romance and excitement. I imagined returning here one day with Luc, prompted by a recent email where he wrote he loved France. He had also mentioned he was writing a song about 'a pretty woman on a train.' Perhaps he would take out his guitar and sing it to me on this very spot in the not-too-distant future? This was Paris and anything could happen.

Jack's small, soft hand woke me from my daydream. I looked down at him and smiled. Then I reached for Marco's hand and in a rare unexpected moment, we all stood silent, looking at the cityscape below; the three of us linked together holding hands.

Chapter 11

Even in the process of writing this book, I feel an inner voice urging me to justify why I left my safe, conventional life in New Zealand. The simple truth is I wanted more from my life. I wanted excitement and change. I wanted to wake up, not knowing what each new day would bring. The famous French tightrope walker Philippe Petit once said, 'Life should be lived on the edge . . . you have to exercise rebellion . . . to see every idea as a true challenge.' From the time I was a little girl, this is how I always wanted to live.

When I decided to travel alone through foreign lands as a single mother, some people called me irresponsible. Many skeptics have since admitted they would never have questioned my trip if I had been travelling with a man. If this had been the case it would certainly have made things easier, for obvious reasons – two people keeping their eye on things, not one but two adults to heave luggage. However, the fact that I didn't have that second person was not going to be my excuse to stay home.

Although most of the friends concerned about my decision to travel alone with the boys genuinely cared about us, I did ask myself if they were secretly envious of my decision to follow my dream? Did they perhaps have dreams of their own they were too afraid to pursue or were they just too afraid of the unknown?

Motherhood can be an impossible balancing act. On the one hand, I want to give my boys the freedom to grow with new challenges as well as having them learn from their mistakes. On the other hand, I am also aware of all the bad things that could happen to them, and a mother's natural instinct is to protect her child.

Consequently, I am constantly warning the boys of potential hazards such as speeding cars when they are crossing the road, the danger of choking with a mouth too full and evil strangers posing as Mr Nice Guy. Losing a child is very real for me after watching my Nan lose my mother, who was only twenty-four. I can't imagine my life without Marco or Jack. I need to see them experience their first girlfriends as teenagers. I want to see them finish school and begin their careers. I need to see them grow into men and have families of their own.

So it was difficult to deal with the fear of losing my boys, or worse having them snatched during our trip. Regardless of the horror stories I heard before leaving New Zealand of things that might occur in big cities, most people we encountered in Paris were friendly and helpful. Yet, I still felt I had to be on constant guard. In a city of twelve million and with a two-year-old boy who loved running this was not an easy task. Luckily, Marco constantly dashed after his runaway brother without complaining. I did consider using safety reins, but I decided against it after seeing Jack's two-year-old cousin constricted by this type of leash during our stay in England. This normally active boy spent his entire visit to Monkey World running on the spot, held back by the reins, trying to catch up to Jack, who was running free. It was upsetting to see this boy who had boundless energy, in a state of captivity similar to the monkeys we were visiting.

On one occasion when we visited the Eiffel Tower, it was Marco not Jack I thought I had lost. We knew if we wanted to climb the tower by the stairs we had to arrive early to be first in the queue of hundreds which quickly established itself there. We arrived at seven thirty, two hours before the ticket office opened and found ourselves standing second in line. However, just before the tower doors opened we were told that we could not leave Jack's pushchair at the bottom for security reasons. This instantly created a dilemma. Marco insisted he walk up the tower, but I could not see myself carrying the pushchair up 172 metres of steps. I tried to persuade Marco to shift into the elevator queue, but he simply refused.

Two Australian girls at the front of the stair-climbing queue overheard me and offered to keep an eye on Marco during the climb. I wanted to become less protective, to take a deep breath and watch from a distance as they picked themselves up after a fall. More importantly, I wanted to be a role model for the boys by doing the same. This was difficult, but I was determined to try.

Consequently, I strapped Jack into his pushchair and rushed over to the elevator tower queue, which was rapidly increasing by the minute. I waved goodbye to Marco and assumed he would be waiting for me at the top. However, after waiting nearly an hour for the elevator I began to regret my decision to be separated from Marco. My mind worked overtime imagining the worst. After all, he was only ten and his obsession for Lego construction made him easy prey for a stranger. Perhaps he could be lured away by pretense to view the behind-the-scenes structure of the tower.

When Marco's face greeted me at the top the relief was exquisite, especially when he hugged me for an extra long time.

At the top of the tower, we were confronted with freezing winds that whipped across our faces. I tried to encourage the boys to admire the expansive view of Paris below us, but after five minutes we were blue with cold and hurried back down. This time we took the stairs together, Marco and I carrying the pushchair between us. I can assure you that seeing the Eiffel Tower from ground level at night with its lights twinkling is far more romantic and involves much less effort or fear.

Jack's pushchair might have been a hindrance at the Eiffel Tower, but it was an item I relied on heavily during our journey, since we covered miles on foot most days. However, its necessity presented regular problems. How many pushchairs can one go through on an eight-month trip around the world? If your name is Rebekah and you have a bad back, bad luck and slight OCD tendencies, the answer is four!

Pushchair #1 – We left New Zealand with a secondhand red umbrella-type pushchair. I thought this style would be handy to fit on the planes and trains. I bought it at a garage sale for twenty-five dollars. This was mistake number one, because during our stay in Canada I discovered that being a cheap brand the wheels did not swivel. This meant placing extra pressure on the handles when turning corners.

I had months of corners ahead of me, so I knew this would pose a problem for my back which had been damaged by excessive exercise earlier in my life. Two forty-minute runs a day had been followed by an aerobic class and a one hour swim at my local pool. Most evenings I would sweat profusely during a two hour Ceroc dance lesson. Nowadays my regime is much less punishing.

Pushchair #2 – The lack of swivel wheels on pushchair #1 forced me to purchase another inexpensive umbrella-type pushchair – blue this time and one with swivel wheels.

The thought of walking around Europe for the next six months more easily made me smile. A few days after we arrived in England my cousin Sarah took Jack for a walk in the new pushchair around the streets of London. After a short time she returned out of breath and said, 'The handles on this pushchair are ridiculously low. I could hardly walk.'

It dawned on me the excruciating back pain I continued to feel was generated by pushchair #2's low-handled-style. Fine if you're a hobbit.

Pushchair #3 – Sarah persuaded me to go to the British baby shop Mothercare to buy pushchair #3. I splashed out on a model that cost fifty-pound – a dream to use in comparison with my two previous models. However, my dream transformed into a nightmare when we took the Parisian metro to the science museum.

Just as we were getting off the train the wheel jammed in between the train and the station. I was on the verge of panic, frightened the doors would close and Jack would be swept away with the train. Thankfully I forced the pushchair onto the platform, though I lost the pushchair's wheel in the process. After the train departed I looked longingly down at the wheel on the tracks below us. A French pass-erby, fearful I was might jump down to retrieve it, pulled me away from the edge, shook his head and pointed to the ticket office upstairs, indicating that I should get help. The stationmaster came to our aid with a special tool that recovered the wheel, which he generously spent half an hour forcing back onto the pushchair.

Pushchair #4 – Sadly, pushchair #3 was never the same after that fateful day in the Parisian metro. It constantly veered to the left, which once again caused excessive strain on my back. By this time we were in Barcelona surrounded by dozens of baby boutiques that oozed style. I could not resist visiting one of the stores a few metres from our apartment while the boys took their *siesta*. I still had four months of pushing and turning to do, so I spent a fortune on the most gorgeous pushchair I have ever seen – a limited edition model designed by Lulu Guinness, plastered with different fonts of the phrase 'I LOVE YOU' in a rainbow of colours. It also had eight wheels that swiveled effortlessly and handles at the perfect height for a mum who is five foot five inches tall.

When I finally returned to New Zealand, my glamorous pushchair attracted much attention as I proudly strolled through Auckland Airport. It was worth every euro.

After recovering from the Eiffel Tower experience and the fear of abduction, I developed a dread of another kind – creepy men in public swimming pools.

Piscine Pontoise was located only a block from our hotel. During regular visits we quickly discovered that like most things in France, this establishment had a strict set of customs:

- Swimming caps had to be bought from the provided vending machines and worn.
- No clothing, aside from swimwear, was allowed (not good for Marco who wanted to cover up his recent weight gain).
- Cold showers had to be taken prior to swimming.
- Locker doors had to be locked, so when you finished swimming you had to wait beside the locker door in the freezing cold, whilst the locker attendant – in typical French fashion – sauntered from three levels below to open it with an air of superiority, of course. All that time I was desperate to get back to the showers to check on my boys who were in there alone with potentially sinister swimmers.

All these regulations seemed simple enough and perhaps they are to the Parisians, but not being fluent in French I had trouble understanding them. We soon learnt if the rules were not adhered to we would be reprimanded by one of the many power-hungry employees on duty.

The most alarming pool experience was the contact I had with a man who tried to pick me up for a drink as I frolicked in the water with Marco and Jack. Initially I was flattered by his attention and invitation, but I knew it would be impossible with nobody to look after the boys. I was about to politely decline. 'Oh thanks so much, unfortunately I can't...' but before I could finish, my admirer, guessing I was refusing, slunk away to the other side of the pool to chat up a young man. Yes, man!

On another visit to the same pool Marco swam off to the deep end. A few minutes later he returned and in between trying to catch his breath told me an elderly man had pulled down his pink Speedos and exposed himself. At the deep end Marco went under the water to try out his recently purchased goggles and apparently saw the man's 'huge pink dangling willy.' Luckily, Marco found it rather amusing and I suggested perhaps it was an accident. Maybe some of my New Zealand friends reading this will tell me that I put my boys in a perilous situation but surely perverts don't just exist in Paris?

Chapter 12

'Come back here!' I screamed as I ran through the Louvre chasing Marco and Jack who were trying to escape. Although I wanted to show the boys as many of the famous tourist sights I could, their indifference to the Mona Lisa made me realise we would all benefit from a change of pace. We needed to stop running from one place to another and really explore the city slowly.

I had started to mimic life back home where I was always running: running to school, running to the shops, running to kindergarten. It took an admission to hospital to have an ovary removed that brought my life to a halt. Similarly, I wanted to put on the brakes during our time in Paris.

So the next morning during our breakfast of croissant and hot chocolate I decided to ditch the guidebook. Instead of visiting three or four sights a day as we did in London I would let Marco plan our day. He chose Paris's Cité des Sciences – a science museum that was hosting the Zizi Sexualle exhibition about puberty. While I knew Marco would understand and appreciate this place, I was worried about Jack. Turned out, because it was a hands-on expo, it was Jack who had the most fun. He played for an hour with a pinball machine which had two sperm racing to a single egg. The highlight of Jack's day was a big red button. Each time he hit it a huge burst of air was released, filling twenty limp, multi-coloured condoms and forcing them to stand erect. When I dragged Jack away from the exhibit Marco kept his distance while his little brother repeatedly yelled, 'I want to blow up the condoms!'

A few minutes later Marco handed me a love poem he had written with the aid of the museum's love poem machine. The exhibition's emphasis on love made me daydream about Luc. When Marco asked, 'Mum, why are you smiling all the time?' I didn't tell him it was because of an email I had just received from Luc:

Dear Rebekah of Paris and the world,

I read each sentence and each word of your email with delight. I imagine you sitting alone with un café au lait et un croissant.

You have all my admiration travelling with two boys. I saw in your eyes on the train how much you are a good mother. You must love very much your boys and it is a great experience for them – a very nice gift for all their lives. Bravo!

I wait for your next email . . . with impatience.

Luc

I thank the French for placing such an importance on love in relation to sex. Where else in the world could a two-year-old, a ten-year-old and their forty-one-year-old mother lie together on a red velvet heart-shaped canopied bed and look up towards a screen that played eighty-eight different love scenes from films like *Doctor Zhivago* and *Dirty Dancing*?

I wish I had more time in my life to slow down and watch movies with my boys on a red velvet couch. The boys, of course, may beg to differ.

Over the years, even the boys' birthdays have become a source of stress. I often feel obliged to create celebrations to match the parties they are invited to. Musical chairs and a Betty Crocker chocolate cake just don't cut it anymore. Instead, children expect treasure hunts with extravagant prizes, a huge selection of home baking or restaurant fare, pony rides, sleepovers with pizza, movies and party bags filled with candy, Lego toys and a parade of helium balloons. Trying to live up to this is not easy, physically or financially, let alone emotionally.

When I look back at Marco's birthday parties up until his tenth, I am shocked to realize how much more is now expected in this world of entertainers, catering and games.

Marco's Birthday Parties:
Age 1   Hired a community hall with 18 friends and family.
Age 2   Party at McDonald's with 15 friends.
Age 3   Mobile animal-farm party with 27 friends.
Age 4   Party at Lollipops Playland with 20 friends.
Age 5   Party at Miniature Train and farm with 16 friends.
Age 6   Ice-skating party with 25 friends.
Age 7   Party at Paint the Earth ceramic paint shop.
Age 8   Movies, cake and friends at cinema with 32 friends.
Age 9   Waterfront restaurant brunch with 8 friends.
Age 10 Sleepover with pizza and a movie with 8 friends.

After Marco's last party I was somewhat relieved to be in Paris for Jack's third birthday. Looking back it had taken days to recover from Marco's last party. Two of Marco's friends had stayed awake the entire night of the sleepover. Then there were the hours spent trying to scrub bubblegum out of the carpet which one of the boys had spat out. As if that wasn't enough, it cost 200 dollars to feed eight ravenous boys and provide them with entertainment in an attempt to prevent them from trashing my house completely.

Thousands of miles away from home I was looking forward to a fun, low-cost, stress-free day for Jack's birthday in Paris. It began with balloons in the hotel room and a game of balloon volleyball. While the boys played, I collected a breakfast of buttery croissants and rich hot chocolate that filled the room with sweet aromas. Jack gobbled his croissant quickly so he could unwrap his present. Remembering his love of music at *The Lion King*, I had managed to find a music store when Jack was having an afternoon nap two days earlier. His face lit up when he saw the tom-tom drum, which he immediately began pounding. Marco and I blocked our ears and prayed there was effective insulation in the hotel walls.

After lounging in our pajamas until mid-morning we went to the local *pâtisserie* for a birthday cake. I found a delicious *gateaux au citron*, which Marco insisted he re-decorate with lashings of lemon icing and chocolate M&Ms making it more appealing for a three-year-old. Jack was delighted with the makeover which had meant very little effort on my part.

After this Marco and Jack watched French cartoons on the television while I dashed to the *supermarché* to buy Camembert, baguettes, ham and cheap French Champagne for a picnic lunch at the Jardin du Luxembourg to share with three guests – Marleen, Wayne and Kylie.

These people had become friends after meeting them on one of our many lunches at the restaurant Chartier. From overhearing their familiar accents I discovered they were from Melbourne and like us, were travelling the world for many months.

Jack immediately bonded with three-year-old Kylie thanks to her huge brown eyes and infectious laugh and by the end of lunch I had invited them to share in Jack's birthday celebration. On our way to meet Kylie and her parents, I felt huge relief knowing that there would only be two three-year-olds, instead of the twenty-seven at Marco's third birthday!

The six of us strolled to the Jardin du Luxembourg with Jack and Kylie laughing together sidestepping the numerous piles of dog excrement littering the pavement. At the park we ignored the signs ordering people to keep off the manicured grass and laid our picnic blanket down. Just as we were about to light the candles on Jack's cake and sing *Happy Birthday*, a gendarme arrived and swiftly ordered us off the grass. His crew-cut hair and dark beady eyes frightened Kylie, who cowered behind Jack. I pleaded with the official, who stood menacingly above us in his dark blue uniform, pointing to the birthday boy, but he showed no compassion. I found it frustrating and contradictory that French dogs can leave piles of excrement all over the pavement, yet set foot on a blade of precious Parisian grass and you could be sent to jail.

We did not let this minor mishap deter us from spending the next two hours lazing on the park's wooden benches in the warm spring sun, while Jack and Kylie played marbles and hopscotch. After lunch we explored Parc de Jeux, one of Paris's largest playgrounds located inside the Jardin du Luxembourg, which was full of swings, slides, sandpits and a flying fox.

Seeking playgrounds that had equipment like climbing frames and other balancing activities became a ritual during our trip around the world. It was some compensation for any physical activity and inter-action he might be missing back home. Language was no barrier for Jack or his French counterparts. Together they jumped, swung and chased each other. I was so happy to see Jack laughing and playing with these new friends. Marco was content to sit quietly reading, undisturbed by his annoying brother. This playground also became a daily opportunity for me to practise my French with the other mothers, who sat watching their children. Another bonus was being able to get fashion tips from these Parisian mothers gorgeously clothed in mini skirts, fur coats and high heels.

The highlight of Jack's birthday occurred in the afternoon, on the Jardin du Luxembourg's lake. We noticed a long queue of small children at a small wooden cabin which had model boats to rent. We quickly joined in and rented two boats which we sailed by a combination of wind and a length of bamboo. Marco, Jack and Kylie spent a very happy time sprinting from one side of the lake to the other, dodging the other children and giggling as they bumped into each other.

In retrospect, Jack's birthday was a huge success. There had been no invitations to buy or post, no huge array of party food to prepare, no expensive location to book, no pre-booked entertainment to pay for, no party bags to buy for demanding children and no utterly-exhausted mother at its conclusion. Instead we had discovered a simple park, a glistening lake, invited three friends to share a picnic lunch and enjoyed a stress-free day full of fun and laughter.

Although I have many supportive and loving friends in New Zealand, I enjoy interaction with complete strangers from other countries. It is stimulating to talk to someone about completely new subjects aside from schooling, colonoscopy, toilet training and house renovations. My friends and I know each other so well there is little mystery left.

I know I could hold back sometimes and not share so many of my inner thoughts, but I like openness, sometimes to a fault. This was the case one evening at a school fundraiser when the disclosure of personal information was encouraged. 'Ladies' Night' was hosted by Jo, a fellow mother and professional stylist, and it began with her advice to the frumpy mums in the audience (Trinny-and-Susannah-style). At the end of the evening there were spot prizes for interesting questions from members of the audience. One of the mums, whom I had confided in earlier, pointed to me while asking, 'What is the worst item of clothing someone could possibly wear?' Jo appeared beside me and shoved a microphone into my hand. Feeling embarrassed but honest I admitted I was wearing my ex-husband's underwear he had given me. When I heard the ripple of sniggers spread through the room I promptly added they were new when I received them. This did not seem to help my case.

Six months later, I took Jack to his first swimming lesson and I sat next to another mother and introduced myself.

'Hello, I'm Rebekah, Jack's mum.'

'I know your name. I remember you vividly from the ladies' night fundraiser,' she replied, smirking.

Travel gave me the opportunity to meet new people and I enjoyed the fact they knew nothing about me. Some I met for only a few minutes, but there was still enough time for them to leave me with a lasting impression.

One of these was Linda whom I met the day I arrived at the Minerve Hotel. Although we only chatted briefly at reception I immediately felt great respect for this brave woman of seventy who was spending a week alone in Paris. She had not let age or lack of company prevent her from embarking on new adventures. It was not until the day of her departure I had another encounter with her. We bumped into each other in the lobby early in the morning as she was settling her bill and she invited us to share breakfast in her room. After enjoying fresh croissants and *café au lait* Linda asked if I could take a photo of her with her father. As I had only ever seen her alone I was surprised. At that moment, she gracefully pointed to a photo of a man with soft eyes and short brown hair, wearing a brown suit and navy tie. Apparently he had always loved Paris, so although he had died a few years before, she wanted to share her Parisian experience with him.

On our last night in Paris my French friend Isabelle, whom we had stayed with on our arrival in Paris, invited me to a movie and dinner. Kylie and her parents kindly offered to babysit Jack and Marco in my hotel room. Comfortably reclining in deep red velvet seats, we watched *Au Bord du Darjeeling* before walking into the nearby Bistro Metro. Here we laughed and talked, recalling old times as we ate steak, *pommes frites* and enjoyed a bottle of French pinot noir. Isabelle insisted we take photos of ourselves to remind myself I did indeed enjoy at least one night out in Paris, single and carefree. Unfortunately, without the aid of a third party, this resulted in many close up shots revealing a recent growth of nasal hair, newly developed wrinkles and the urgent need to bleach my upper-lip hair.

In the process, an elderly man, sitting at an outside table, knocked on the window and offered to help. During the photo shoot, we learnt Joseph was a seventy-five-year-old American spending six months in Paris alone in a rented apartment. As with Linda, this encounter with Joseph left me feeling optimistic about old age, because he had not let age or being single stand in the way of his dream to live in Paris. Instead, he quoted George Bernard Shaw's words, 'We don't stop playing because we grow old; we grow old because we stop playing.'

I met Pierre when the boys and I were dining at one of our favourite Chinese and Thai restaurants in Paris, Le Palais de la Griserie. The *Soupe Pekingese* (hot sour soup) was superb. On this occasion Pierre, a fellow diner sitting alone, kept smiling at us. At the end of his meal he detoured by our table and began speaking to me in French. I tried to converse, but he had enough alcohol to be unaware that French was not my first language. He spoke so fast I could not fully understand him. Nevertheless, I was able to gather he had not seen his son for about twelve years as a result of a custody battle he had lost. His words soon turned to tears and Marco and Jack sat in quiet disbelief as this complete stranger opened his heart to three travellers from New Zealand.

As we were about to leave, Pierre insisted he buy us dessert. I looked at my watch as we were planning to catch the metro to the Arc de Triomphe. At that moment I remembered John Lennon's words written in my autograph book by a friend, 'Never forget – life is what happens to you while you're busy making other plans.' Then I noticed the boys' faces begging me to accept his kind offer. Hmmm.

'Oui. J'accept. Merci.'

Marco and Jack invited Pierre to sit down and help make a house of cards using the sugar sachets on the table. In between eating mouthfuls of creamy vanilla ice cream and chocolate sauce, Marco whispered to me, 'We are lucky, eh, Mum?' My heart warmed and I smiled and nodded as I gazed at my boys' happy faces and watched them lick their plates clean.

Yes, we were all lucky, but I felt the luckiest.

Chapter 13

Although I had resolved to slow down in Paris, I still found myself being caught up in the hustle and bustle of city life. Paris was full of so many wonderful restaurants and iconic tourist attractions, which were just too tempting to resist.

Realising we were nearly halfway through our adventure, with only four months left before we would return to New Zealand, I wanted to slow down even more. I dreamed of staying in a sleepy French village where all the demands of city life were nonexistent, where I could rise each morning and amble my way to the local *pâtisserie* to buy pastries and warm baguettes with morning coffee, with no plans of sightseeing for the rest of the day. I needed a place where I could enjoy the local *marché*, purchasing delicacies to eat in my garden, while enjoying the midday sun with a chilled Beaujolais, then a *siesta*. Alet-les-Bains was the perfect setting for this.

Nestled between small mountains, Alet is a tiny village in southern France's Languedoc region. It supports a population of 500 and hasn't changed much since the ninth century, apart from the fact it no longer has gory religious conflict. On the second day, when we visited the local tourist information bureau, a man named Nicolas said, 'From 1208 the Catholic Church had hung, or burnt at the stake an estimated 500,000 Languedoc men, women and children during its crusade against the Cathar religion.'

Although this was ancient history, the village still perpetuated traditions from ancient times. The morning after our arrival we witnessed one of them when young locals gathered at midnight to raid homes of plants, window shutters, statues and rubbish bins. Next morning, Alet's medieval square was overflowing with the 'stolen' possessions. Dazed locals walked around the piles of items searching for their belongings. Nicolas later enlightened me that this was the villagers' custom of welcoming the beginning of May. It seemed extraordinary this tradition was tolerated when back home the police would have been called to arrest anyone trespassing on private property. However, these youths executed the pranks with care, not causing any damage, so no one appeared to complain.

Time stood still in this quaint village so my life began to mirror its pace. Even the chores of everyday life became pleasurable. The replenishment of water bottles with thermal mineral water was obtained free from a local Roman-style water supply where locals congregated each morning to chat. The water had been bottled for over 120 years, making it one of the oldest brands in France. When an elderly woman informed me that spa water was good for obesity I vowed to drink buckets full.

The spa was only a few metres from Les Figuiers, the three-storied house I rented for two weeks. It had four bedrooms, two living areas, two kitchens and three bathrooms. Each room offered glorious views of mountains, misty mornings and sun-hazed afternoons.

Les Figuiers was booked on the internet before leaving New Zealand. Knowing that most of our trip would be spent in tiny apartments or miniscule hotel rooms, I thought it would be a treat for us to enjoy a house with large garden; a place we could spread out and enjoy some personal space. Now Marco could enter the bathroom without having to confront his mother's leopard-skin-print underwear drying on the shower rail, a house where I could walk freely without stepping on a sharp piece of Jack's Lego. However, before we left Paris, Stephan had phoned asking if Marco could visit him for a month in Burkina Faso, West Africa, where he was working. Although I was disappointed Marco would miss out on the Languedoc region of France, I knew the experience he would have in Africa would be far greater, so when Marco said, 'Please let me go Mum. Dad told me I will see wild animals,' of course I agreed. However, I made sure I taught Marco some survival tactics, a result of my nightmarish safari with Stephan eleven years earlier.

It was during my first trip to Africa to meet Stephan that we had spent two days and nights in Benin's Penjari Park viewing numerous animals: lions, monkeys, hippos, giraffes and antelope. On day two we drove from the Tata Somba Lodge in the village of Natitango across the park to the village of Porga. But, as we stepped into Stephan's 4WD work vehicle some locals informed us that fluid was dripping out of the engine. Being the unmechanically-minded 'expert' that he was, Stephan took a quick look and when he failed to discover the source of the leak made the decision to ignore the advice. It was a minor problem, he assured me.

Initially, we drove along the pot-holed dirt road enjoying the scenery and wild animals that we spotted along the way. Thirty-five kilometres from our destination our car came to a sudden halt. At that point Stephan undertook a closer inspection, discovering that the transmission fluid was what had been leaking and it was now completely gone. We were in the middle of nowhere and to put it bluntly, we were stuffed.

Our unplanned stop occurred late afternoon, so we had no choice but to sleep in the car. Neither of us was terribly concerned at this stage. We were certain another vehicle would pass us the following day and tow us to our lodge. However, I was terrified to leave the vehicle to go to the toilet after noticing the numerous lion footprints surrounding the car.

I woke in good spirits considering our situation. Stephan, who by then felt the depth of our predicament, woke annoyed. By midday my upbeat mood had also wilted. No cars had passed. We had no food and only three bottles of water – inadequate considering the extremely hot forty-five degree temperature.

'We need to start walking,' I told Stephan.

'No! I've always been taught to stay by your vehicle so rescuers can find you and it's a nine hour walk at least,' he replied.

'What if no one comes? What then? We've hardly any water left.'

'Okay,' said Stephan. 'You stay in the car and I'll go and get help.'

'No way!' I replied.

He didn't argue with me anymore.

We made spears with nearby sticks and I grabbed the car's fire extinguisher, our only defense against the lions. We covered our bodies with ripped-up car seat covers to protect ourselves from the scorching heat and set off on the dusty track our car should have taken.

The lion footprints increased as we moved further along the track, intensifying my feeling of dread. I tried to keep calm by reminding myself that lions sleep during the day. Moreover, I also remembered lions only attack if startled, so I made Stephan sing *You Are My Sunshine* with me as we walked to pre-warn the animals. But it didn't take long before the hot air wore down our voices. Our pace was quite rapid for the first two hours, before dehydration began to slow us down, especially Stephan, whose larger mass needed a lot more fluid than mine. By the time we had walked for five hours we had only one bottle of water left. Stephan was swerving as he walked and kept asking to stop and rest under the occasional tree we passed. I knew if we did he wouldn't get up again – and we still had another four hours ahead of us. What made our situation worse was the knowledge that the lions would soon wake from their afternoon nap. I kept encouraging Stephan, knowing if we gave up now we could both end up as dinner steaks.

After five and a half hours of walking, a Land Rover full of hunters returning from a day's outing came towards us. We were saved! Stephan was so overjoyed by the sight of rescuers he dropped his spear and ran into the middle of the road waving his arms frantically.

Stephan's swollen, dehydrated tongue made him unable to speak, but he managed to mouth the words, 'thank you for supporting me,' as he looked affectionately towards me in the back of the Land Rover.

We waited for three days at the hunters' lodge for our vehicle to be recovered and fixed. During that time no other cars came through the park. It was frightening to realise that we almost stayed put.

Months later Stephan told me, 'that was the day I knew you were the woman I wanted to marry.'

Marco's equipment list driving for with Stephan in Africa:
- 87 bottles of water
- 2 x fire extinguishers
- 1 x mechanic
- Bottle of SPF 99 suntan lotion
- Long-sleeve clothing, long pants and sun hat
- 4 weeks supply of food
- 1 x tranquilizer gun

Marco's trip to Africa meant that Jack and I would be rattling around in a huge home, which slept eight and could be lonely and extravagant. It was not long after Stephan's call that we met Kylie and her parents in Paris's Chartier restaurant and, as you may remember, I invited them to Jack's birthday party in the Jardin de Luxenbourg. By the end of the party, I had also invited them to join Jack and me in Alet.

Wayne, Marleen and Kylie were travelling on a tight budget and since I had already paid for Les Figuiers, I offered them free accommodation if they could contribute towards the cost of food. The offer to relative strangers to share a house with me for a fortnight may sound risky, but at the time I saw it as an opportunity to have some adult company. I looked forward to sharing meals together, cooking and eating and having adult conversations especially about travel, as they were halfway through a six-month trip around the world.

I was also relieved Jack would have a friend to play with for a couple of weeks and Kylie and Jack had become instant friends. One of the best rooms in the house for the children was the games room and while they played Lego and table tennis, Wayne, Marleen and I were free to cook all afternoon. The fully equipped kitchen contained blenders, food processors, Sabatier knives and a library of mouth-watering recipe books, including my favourite, Julia Child's *Mastering the Art of French Cooking*.

The kitchen's French doors opened onto a large, flat garden flush with pink rose bushes and cherry trees bearing juicy, sweet fruit. This outdoor paradise created another place where Jack and Kylie could play. A yellow plastic bucket of water, some plastic boats we found in the bottom of the garden and two baby dolls occupied them for hours. In the late afternoon sun, Wayne, Marleen and I reclined in deck chairs talking, reading and eating ripe Brie accompanied by chilled glasses of pinot gris.

Loud banging on Les Figuiers' wooden door woke me from our first afternoon nap. While Wayne and Marleen seemed oblivious to the noise, I ran downstairs and opened the thick, heavy door.

'*Bonjour*,' chirped a petite elderly woman, whose black-dyed hair looked rather severe against the soft pink sequined blouse she wore.

'*Je suis Freya*. Your neighbor.'

'Oh hello,' I said, trying to adjust my eyes to the bright afternoon sun. 'It's nice to meet you. Would you like to come in?'

'No. I don't have time. Here, take these,' she ordered, as she handed me a plate piled high with sweet pastries she had cooked to welcome us.

Later, I learnt the pastries were an Algerian treat called *makroud*, honey-covered pastry filled with sweet almonds. Freya was originally from Algeria but like two million other Algerians, had fled the country before Algeria gained its independence from France. It didn't take long for Freya's *makrouds* to be consumed and from that day on, we would return from walks to find plates of Algerian treats on our doorstep.

The most popular dish of Freya's was her *merguez*, spicy mutton sausages. She made thirty-three on the first Saturday morning of our stay.

'I will come back,' she told us as she handed me a large plastic container filled with the red-coloured sausages smelling of fennel and garlic.

'Can you barbeque the *merguez* at five?' Freya asked.

How could we refuse?

Freya arrived at five o'clock sharp with her son Christophe, his wife Anne and their son Lenny. The nine of us wolfed down the whole batch in less than half an hour.

Wayne, Marleen and I shared a mutual love of food. This was evident from the moment we arrived at Les Figuiers when we sat down at the kitchen table and began flicking through the pile of recipe books. It was clear we would eat like kings. Every day of the week each village in the region had a market day. The five of us would visit a different one each day, buying fresh organic products for the feasts we'd cook on our return.

Esperaza's market was our favourite. A ten-minute train ride would transport us from Alet to a village renowned for its 'alternative life-style,' reflected by the market and its English-type residents who flocked to the area in funky retro clothing. The food and ambience was vibrant and colourful. Stalls displayed free-range eggs, homemade sausages, cheese and organic meat straight from the farm. Being close to the Spanish border, this area had a strong Spanish influence. The choice of twenty different Catalan olives, with free samples on offer, attracted anyone to linger at the counter. My favourites were the juicy green ones stuffed with garlic. Lounging in the hot sun, Marleen, Wayne and I nibbled on the olives and sipped cheap *sangria*, while Jack and Kylie danced to the live music performance. Before long, the aroma of *paella* drifted our way and we ran to join the long queue in front of Jose's caravan for a delicious lunch.

During the first week we turned Les Figuier's kitchen into a chef's paradise and produced French onion soup, spaghetti, oven-roasted rabbit, steak with sauce *poivre vert*, *coq au vin*, roast pork, onion and goat's cheese tart and *pomme au gratin*.

In addition to our own cooking, we enjoyed frequent lunches at a nearby restaurant, Auberge de la Corneilla. Fairy lights twinkled within the dark dining room, creating a romantic ambience. This setting made an unusual backdrop for the large table of local workmen sitting beside us in fluorescent work vests, enjoying a daily three-course lunch with wine. *Vive le Français* in their determination to incorporate pleasure into their daily lives, even during work hours.

I have found because I am single I am rarely invited to dinner parties. I mean real adult dinner parties (the ones without kids) – where people sit at a large table discussing grown-up subjects. Other single women have confirmed this same observation. One said a so-called friend blatantly suggested it is because of an imbalance in numbers around the table.

I find my lack of social outings frustrating because after being with my children all day it would be stimulating to share a conversation with a group of adults about subjects other than nappies and after-school activities. I would like to have hosted my own dinner parties, however, the thought of coming home from work only to begin preparing food in the tiny two-bedroom apartment I purchased before leaving, and with two young boys to consider, did not seem much fun.

During my time in Alet, although I remained solo the difference was not only did I have a kitchen and dining table fit for a feast, I also had fellow gourmands, Marleen and Wayne, who loved to share cooking and preparation. So I suggested we host a 'real' dinner party and the guest of honour should be Nicolas de Leon.

I first met Nicolas when I was in my fast-paced Paris mode. I entered the village's tourism information bureau where Nicolas worked on our second day in Alet to ask, 'Where can I find an internet café?'

'The village library,' he replied.

'Fantastic, where is it?' I inquired.

'Just next door, but it is closed now.'

'Oh, what time does it open?'

'Two o'clock in the afternoon.'

'Okay, I'll come back after lunch then.'

'No, don't. I forgot to say two o'clock on Friday.'

'But it's only Tuesday.'

'Yes.'

'What?!'

It had already been three days since I'd last written to Luc. If I didn't email him soon he might think I wasn't interested anymore. Nicolas sensed my frustration and told me I could use the bureau's computer to retrieve my emails if I was quick. I rushed to his desk and quickly opened my Gmail. A message from Luc was waiting.

Hello Rebekah . . .

You really intrigue me Rebekah. I really want to meet you in June. I think we have no choice now.

I had already noticed you were a romantic woman . . . first in the train when you look few seconds at me . . . and also when I speak to you by phone. There is something in your voice. I never forget a voice and I can detect often some particularity. I'm not afraid with this romantic side. I think I have also this side with me.

What is your passion? What is the colour you prefer? What is the colour of your eye? What is the best book of your life? The best food, the best drink? What is your secret dream?

Luc

As I made daily visits with Jack to check my emails from Luc, Nicolas quickly became our friend. Ironically, although he worked at the tourism bureau, he spent little of his day actually talking to tourists about local places of interest. Instead, most of the day, I would see him leaning on the window ledge of the bureau, puffing on a cigar and chatting to fellow villagers.

Nicolas's long black greasy hair slicked back into a ponytail and his thick dark-rimmed glasses made him look as if he was working for Black Sabbath rather than the French Department of Tourism. His bachelor pad clutter, black painted walls and crumbling ceiling were consistent with this image. Consequently, I was shocked when he opened the door to his spare room one evening when he had invited Jack and me for dinner. It was set up for his mother who often came to stay and it was spotless. A single bed was placed in the centre and was made up with meticulously ironed white sheets. A small crystal vase holding freshly-cut pink roses sat on top of the wooden bedside cabinet. Unlike the rest of the house, there was not a scrap of mess or clutter to be seen: no piles of magazines stacked to the ceiling, no electronic parts waiting to be fixed, there were no dirty cups or posters of naked women. This was a room arranged for an adored mother.

Jack and I looked forward to our regular visits to the *Office du Tourisme*. My daily use of his internet was followed by hours sharing the window ledge and eating a large container of vanilla ice cream from the village store across the road which the three of us shared

139

with three spoons. Most of all, we loved listening to the animated way Nicolas told stories about life in the village. In spite of his very rapid French, he still managed to have us in hysterics. Apparently, during a recent *Tour de France*, Nicolas waited four and a half hours on the side of a barricaded road only minutes from his home while the cyclists rode past. After hours of extreme frustration, he scribbled some words on a piece of old cardboard and for the last hour held his placard high which read, 'You are all druggies!' The French never seem afraid of saying what they feel.

I wanted to treat Nicolas to dinner because, in addition to letting me use his computer, he also lent us his car one day to explore the local region. Marleen, Wayne, Jack, Kylie and I made the most of it by visiting a thermal mineral pool in the nearby town of Rennes-les-Bains. There we soaked up the wonderful warmth of the water and sun where bathers as far back as Roman times had come to use the natural hot spring water as a cure for rheumatism and skin problems. Nicolas also drove us to and from the *supermarché* many times in a neighboring town so Wayne, Marleen and I could purchase supplies. It was much easier taking our twelve bags of shopping home by car, than walking back to Les Figuiers laden with heavy bags and trying to keep Kylie and Jack under control on a hot dusty road that had numerous trucks whooshing past and no footpath. However, being Nicolas's passenger was not a comfortable experience. Large clouds of dust rose from the old seats every time somebody moved and as Nicolas sped along, he overtook and swore at the other drivers who weren't keeping up with him, refusing to slow down even when we warned him of four *gendarmes* doing speed checks. Accompanying his crazy driving skills was Van Halen blaring out of the speakers, though Jack, being a fellow rocker, loved it. For me it was the perfect recipe for a migrane.

Regardless of stressful car rides to the *supermarché*, Wayne, Marleen and I decided that we would go all out for Nicolas. We would cook a feast that would pay tribute to Nicolas's generosity with the internet, his stories, ice cream and his car. Onions were caramelized, pastry was rolled, goat's cheese was crumbled, sirloin of beef was rubbed with garlic and olive oil and potatoes were smothered with cream and cheese. Knowing how important cheese is to the French, we bought Pélardon, Roquefort and Bleu des Causses – the most delectable cheeses made in the Languedoc region to enjoy after dessert.

Unfortunately, we were unaware we were cooking for possibly the only Frenchman who was allergic to cheese! Poor Nicolas. He sat at the table with a last-minute improvised cold plate of salami and olives, while we dug into our delicious goat's cheese and onion tart and roast beef dinner. Luckily, Nicolas gulped down the bottle of Muscat, a sweet local wine. After the main course Nicolas reached into his canvas bag and produced a *tarte aux pommes* and *madeleine* cakes for dessert.

'I thought you were a diabetic?' I said as Nicolas began to devour a large slice of *tarte* with a second glass of sugary Muscat.

'Oui, c'est correct,' he replied, smiling as he reached for a second slice.

If I could name the highlight of our time in Alet it would have to be dancing at the village hall on Sunday afternoons. While Marleen, Wayne and I were relaxing in the garden on our first Sunday afternoon in the village we heard music, which finally got the better of me.

'Come on everyone,' I said. 'Let's go and find out where that music is coming from!'

The five of us followed the cobblestone streets weaving our way around corners until we came to the village hall. The others waited outside while I went in to investigate. Inside I felt I had stepped back in time. At three o'clock in the afternoon, the hall was packed with couples young and old, dressed in floral dresses and neatly pressed suits and ties. They were waltzing the afternoon away to the rhythm of a live accordion accompanying a young singer dressed to kill in a sequined skin-tight dress, with long blonde hair to her waist. I eagerly ran back outside and grabbed Wayne, Marleen and the kids.

'Quick!' I said. 'Come inside! It's fantastic!'

Kylie and Jack ran straight onto the dance floor and soon became giddy as they twirled around the room without a care in the world. An eighty-year-old lady in a fuchsia pink dress then moved them to one side so they did not collide with the more serious older dancers. From that time on, Sundays couldn't come soon enough.

Dancing on Sundays made me realise how few times I dance as an adult. I'm not counting boogying in the living room with children to The Wiggles. There are not many opportunities. Occasionally I'll dance at a wedding or perhaps I will let loose at a friend's fortieth? I can't think of too many other times.

One evening I went to a singles' ball in New Zealand. *The Bachelor's* Jason and Molly hosted it, travelling from America on an Air New Zealand promotional flight full of single Americans eager to find love in New Zealand. There were supposed to be about 500 potential love interests present, so after persuading a couple of girlfriends to come with me for moral support, I booked tickets online and then went shopping.

I went all out for the occasion and bought a red satin dress with matching red bra and knickers (I was certainly not going to wear Stephan's old undies on this night). I had huge hopes I might meet the man of my dreams.

I even went to my local printing shop and had 100 'calling cards' printed. Pink ones that read 'Rebekah, lady in red,' including my phone number. I did not want to miss a single opportunity and planned to give a card to any man that caught my eye, or might be standing in the queue.

I strutted into the ballroom, slightly ahead of my friends and scanned the room for potential targets. The low lighting made it difficult, but I noticed a group of singles who had also arrived early. Sweet perfume and musky cologne were noticeable as I approached and accepted a glass of sparkling wine. Feeling quite confident in my new silk dress, I handed out three cards within the first five minutes.

Four hours later I sat slumped and depressed in the back of a taxi with the other ninety-seven cards still tucked away in my handbag. Unfortunately, the organizers had offered tickets to anyone on a first-in, first-served basis with no age limit or set of criteria for the event. As a result, groups of much younger beauties in their twenties arrived ready to party and upstage us. Dressed in skimpy miniskirts exposing their lean bronzed legs, they swarmed like bees around the men in my age bracket. My friends and I never had a chance.

I did dance that night, with my girlfriends, but it was not quite what I had anticipated. After sashaying around the dance floor, trying unsuccessfully to catch the eye of available men, I couldn't believe what eventually caught my attention. There on the enormous buffet table stood a huge *bain-marie* of creamy, steaming-hot mashed potato. With a large plateful each, three of us retreated to a dark corner where we found solace in culinary pleasure and after several returns I had completely lost interest in our original campaign.

Chapter 14

In getting to know strangers at such close quarters I should have expected some irritations sooner or later. Such was the case, though the detail does not need recounting. Let's just say a lot of wine was consumed and an obscene amount of cleaning products were applied to kitchen and bathroom surfaces – all activities occurring well past midnight.

A more difficult situation developed when Marleen and Wayne frequently reprimanded Jack while believing that their Kylie could do no wrong. I bit my tongue often, until day thirteen when Marleen and I were cooking *coq au vin*. Jack suddenly let out a bloodcurdling scream in the dining room and I found Kylie strangling him with both hands. As her fingernails sank into Jack's flesh she began screaming too. Marleen remained in the kitchen and couldn't see the unfolding crisis, yet she immediately jumped to the conclusion Jack was to blame and shouted, 'Stop screaming, Jack!'

'Jack's screaming because your daughter's strangling him,' I bellowed.

'Jack, don't scream,' Marleen responded calmly. 'If Kylie does this again, just say, "please Kylie, stop doing that! I do not like it."'

Not an easy thing to do when someone's hands are gripped tightly around your throat.

These daily annoyances which occurred while sharing a house with virtual strangers were soon forgotten when Jack and I sat in the quiet, empty house having farewelled Wayne, Marleen and Kylie. After two weeks they were now leaving for the south of France. Regardless of our differences, Marleen, Wayne and Kylie were a family I would happily spend time with again, especially in such a unique French location, where wine is cheap and food plentiful. On reflection, their bad habits seemed insignificant in the scheme of things. After all, they could have been so much worse.

Much of our accommodation was booked via the internet before leaving New Zealand and I had anticipated that after spending two weeks in Alet we'd need a change of scenery. As a result I booked an apartment in Espéraza, a small market village two train stops away from Alet. Nicolas arrived half an hour later and drove us there. However, when he drove off leaving us in the cramped dark home which was to be our new accommodation for the next two weeks, I wish I'd taken heed of Jane Austen's words, 'How often is happiness destroyed by preparation, foolish preparation?' I had paid in advance for small, shuttered windows that struggled to lighten the dark miniscule kitchen. The internet description failed to mention the staircase to the bedrooms and living area was practically vertical, which was a worry with Jack. There was no garden, or outside play area. Instead the front door opened onto a busy street, which was frequented by loud drunk teenagers and drivers who failed to slow down for pedestrians. When I thought about what we'd left behind I sat down and cried.

Jack sat next to me and started rubbing my tummy.

'Do you feel better now?' he asked.

I had to change my mood. I didn't want to be sad around Jack, so that meant I had to get out of this claustrophobic setting. Jack and I set off for a walk around the town and came across an art exhibition at the home of two middle-aged American women who had lived in Espéraza for ten years. Within moments of our meeting their warm greeting triggered a flood of tears but when Jack started to have a tantrum after one of the women forbade him from eating the nibbles provided for adult visitors, we made a quick exit.

Homesickness for Alet overwhelmed me as we returned to our new accommodation. I sat in the gloomy, small room and felt alone.

You'd think I was used to being by myself, especially as I was often alone during my childhood, tending to the home and cooking dinner while Nanny worked to support us. Although tough at times, this upbringing ultimately shaped me into the independent woman I am. I learnt very quickly that anything I wanted in life had to be earned. Consequently, when I worked as an international flight attendant, I religiously saved my wages, determined to buy a home of my own, which I did at the age of twenty-one. This was in sharp contrast to many of my female friends, whom I called the 'Gold and Diamond Brigade.' While I was living on a tight budget, they would spend the bulk of their salary on clothing and jewellery, with the hope that a man would one day come along and meet all their other material needs.

I have certainly never expected my Prince Charming would arrive on his white horse and rescue me, even when the idea seemed tremendously appealing. Yet, it would be nice to know that while I am reading bedtime stories, someone else was washing the dinner dishes and making a cup of tea. I just wish life could be easier, but most of all I craved adult company.

Wiping away my tears Jack whispered, 'Let's eat ice cream with Nicolas!'

'What a wonderful idea,' I replied.

Back into the bright daylight with Jack in hand we searched for a pay phone. I then rang Nicolas in tears and begged him to come that night for dinner. I was shocked when only twenty minutes later he was banging on my door. I jumped out of my chair, wiped away my tears and gave him a huge hug. Nicolas's company over spaghetti bolognaise boosted my mood, but there was no escaping my yearning for the beautiful three-story house and garden nestled within the tranquil mountains of Alet. Moreover, while watching Nicolas teach Jack to wash the dishes, I realised what I really longed for were my newfound friends and a sense of belonging.

Early next morning I rang the owners of Les Figuiers, Steve and Sandra, a British couple from Bristol. Between loud and uncontrollable sobbing I explained I had already paid fully for my two-week stay in Espéraza, but I would be prepared to forfeit my money (again!) if they would consider a reduced rate for more time in Alet. They agreed. I was relieved and rang Nicolas, who was waiting for my call. He assured me he would be there in half an hour to collect us. Nicolas's devotion was something I had always dreamed of having from a father or a brother. I felt protected.

Driving back to Alet I thanked Nicolas for coming to get us at such short notice. He turned down Judas Priest and told me that on his way home from dinner the previous night he had made up his mind to bring me back and had rung his boss late that evening to say he would need some time off the next day because, 'Rebekah needed saving!'

As he dropped us off at Les Figuiers he yelled, 'I'll come back for dinner tonight. No cheese!'

'Of course,' I replied, laughing.

Inside I noticed a large blue china plate on the kitchen bench. It was heaped with *makrouds*, their melted-honey-coating glistening in the midday sun. Jack and I took the plate out into the garden and sat down on a blanket underneath the cherry tree and began eating.

PART 7

Spain

Chapter 15

'Are we going to Spain to see bullfights?' Marco asked as our train chugged past a bullfighting poster on the outskirts of Barcelona.

'No Marco, we are going to find my father.'

From what my Nan told me, my mother had always been a keen traveller. From a young age she visited many European countries, eager to learn their language and to immerse herself in their culture. The most significant trip my mother ever took was to Spain in 1965, when she was nineteen. She returned to England a few weeks later, to discover she was pregnant.

When my mother died four years after my birth she left no information about my father. No photo. No name. Nothing. At school I could never answer the other children's questions about my dad and when the class bully called me a 'bastard' what could I say? I didn't believe Nanny when she said, 'I don't know anything about your father.' I thought she wanted to keep his identity secret so he didn't steal me from her. As I grew up I accepted she was telling the truth. By then she had no reason to lie to me but as I grew older this lack of knowledge frustrated and angered me. How could my mother have denied me such important information? When I moved from my twenties into my thirties I imagined my mother had been preoccupied with her failing health. Furthermore, being so young, perhaps she had not considered the possibility that she might actually die. I am sure she'd intended to tell me about her love affair with my father when I was older.

Sadly, that never happened. As a result, I have spent my life imagining what my father looked like and what kind of person he was. I think I have some idea about a few of his traits because I am very different from my mother. My mother, for instance, was a straight-A student, receiving some of the highest marks in the county. She was fluent in French, German, Italian, Russian and Latin. At the same time she was talented at art, studied physics and chemistry and won a place at university before she had even taken her A-levels. Sadly by then, she was too sick to attend. I wish I had inherited my mother's intelligence. Yes, I have achieved success at university, but it has come from tons of hard work. I am certainly no genius like my mother.

In addition, my mother was tall with long, slender limbs. Her lengthy dark hair sat gracefully upon her head in a simple French twist. In photos in Nanny's album my mother is poised and elegant in her modest yet stylish summer dresses. So, from my appearance, I am guessing my father was short, hairy and muscular, with very pronounced calf muscles.

As for my father's personality, I'd like to think he was loud and vivacious like me because I am certainly no wallflower and don't suffer from my mother's agoraphobia. Though I am not immune from anxiety, mine is just related to Obsessive Compulsive Disorder. An instance of this is the dread I feel when someone walks into my house with shoes on, imagining they may have stepped in urine in a public toilet. Then there's my need to move tables three or four times in cafes because the first two tables were too close to the kitchen, or too near to the door, or too dimly lit, or too small. I have another habit of buying identical items of clothing, in case the first item might one day wear out, which is why you'd notice three pairs of leopard-printed jeans in my wardrobe from Guess clothing in Montreal. Together they cater for every contingency.

I like to think I am a fusion of my mother and father – a slightly neurotic, wide-calved, leopard-print attired, hard-working, spirited go-getter.

Although as a young girl I felt so loved by Nanny it was hard not to feel I had missed out on some really important encounters: the warmth and security of a father's embrace? A daddy's kiss? The exchange of laughter after being thrown in the air? I would watch my friends with their fathers, and my longing to experience my own father's affection would increase.

Each night I would dream the same dream – about what it would be like to have a father. In the fantasy, I imagined being lifted from my bed and held in the strong arms of my father. When I cried, he would gently brush his fingers over my forehead while singing *Frère Jacques* until I drifted back to sleep.

With children of my own, the desire to have a father deepened. It was as if this missing link became much more significant because my two boys would never know their grandfather. To compensate I imagined them in his Spanish villa, surrounded by olive trees, the three of them in his little kitchen cooking *paella* and learning Spanish.

Prompted by these daydreams, before leaving New Zealand I searched through my mother's belongings in an old brown leather suitcase Nanny had given me just before she died. I found letters my mother had written to Nanny from Spain during her 1965 vacation. Combing my way through the crinkled papers, I found mention of four different Spanish boys my mother had met at that time:

Spanish Boy #1: 12th August 1965 – *I am looking forward to tomorrow as I am going out with this Spanish boy (the artist). He is very good looking and tall! Most of the Spanish boys are very small.*

Spanish Boy #2: 29th August 1965 – *On Wednesday we went to the beach and I wore my bikini. Very few people wear bikinis (in fact this day I saw no-one in one) so all the boys (and old men) looked at me as they walked past. When I went in the sea a crowd of Spanish boys talked to me and I spent the afternoon sunbathing in their dingy! One of them wanted to take me dancing but I couldn't go as I only had shorts and no skirt.*

Spanish Boy #3: 1st September 1965 – *Last night we went to a club and I met a super Spanish boy named Jose-Miguel. He is very good-looking and is a university student. I am meeting him tomorrow.*

Spanish Boy #4: 2nd September 1965 – *On Sunday we went to a nightclub until 10 or 11. I danced with a basketball player who plays for Real Madrid and is quite famous. On Monday I wore my bikini again on the beach and again met the boys with the dingy. I am going out with one of them this evening. He is very nice, aged 25 and called Jose.*

Even though I hadn't originally planned to go to Spain, as I placed the letters back in the suitcase I decided there was still time to make changes in the itinerary.

Exploring Spain might be a chance to feel close to the father I had never met.

Unlike my short stay in Espéraza, this time I felt at home immediately inside the small, furnished apartment I'd rented for two weeks in the centre of Barcelona. The neighbourhood was called Eixample and was home to the local Catalans. This modernista flat, owned by a woman working in Columbia for the United Nations, housed Persian carpets, bright coloured décor and walls plastered with books and modern art. I not only appreciated her books for the ambience they created, but also for the pleasure of reading. Books had been too heavy to include in our luggage while we were travelling, so each day, when Jack took his daily *siesta*, Marco and I retired to the blue and orange tiled terrace and consumed book after book.

While I felt lucky to be staying in a place owned by a book lover, the choice of artwork embarrassed ten-year-old Marco. Had he been a few years older he might have relished the explicit images of naked women. Instead, the numerous painted images of breasts and vaginas were an unwelcomed form of sex education for the poor lad in the early stages of puberty.

Apart from the décor, the books and the art, the apartment was extremely small. We could hardly swing a cat in the teeny kitchen, let alone cook. However, this forced us to spend much of our time looking for suitable places to eat, which wasn't hard given that our apartment was located near the La Boqueria Market at Las Ramblas. This market housed over 500 food stalls, where tourists and chefs from local restaurants came daily to buy the freshest Catalan produce. Food in Barcelona is hugely important in the lives of its inhabitants and it is said that Gaudi took inspiration from the triangular-shaped morel mushrooms for his architecture in the city.

We quickly embraced the Spanish lifestyle of afternoon *siestas* and late-night eating, often not returning to our apartment until eleven o'clock at night. Our favourite restaurant was Monchos, a beachside eatery which served huge bowls of *paella* and large stainless-steel pots of steamed mussels cooked in garlic and wine. Inevitably, by the end of a meal, Jack's shirt would be completely dripping with the seafood sauce. Surely we must have Spanish genes!

Walking back late at night from restaurants, it was wonderful to see a metropolis buzzing with thousands of locals, still out on the street even mid-week. This was probably because most of the apartments, like ours, were small. A local taxi driver told me the apartments are so tiny because, 'Barcelonian inhabitants live on the street and only go to their apartments to sleep.' Less space meant fewer things, which meant more money to spend on experiences. Travel began to teach me that all a person really needs is someone to love and a suitcase, or in my case, two children and ten pieces of luggage!

Although we spent little time inside it didn't take long before we discovered that directly below us lived an elderly woman who was intolerant of Jack's screaming and banging on the wooden floor. A few days into our visit we received a call from the manager of the apartment informing us that this neighbour had rung numerous times to complain. Although I could understand the old woman's plight, I thought she was a tad cantankerous considering we were out of the apartment enjoying the city for at least eight hours each day. Subsequently, we used her complaints as an excuse to stay out even longer.

Ornate buildings, loud voices and brightly-coloured clothing filled the streets – and I fitted right in!

This was a change from the way I often felt at home in New Zealand. I'll never forget the time when an old boyfriend once ordered me to, 'Stop laughing so loud!' That was the end of him! Then there were countless occasions when Marco refused to be seen with me because of my outrageously colourful outfits. In one instance after Marco's basketball game he ignored me, even when I approached to congratulate him on his team's win. On the way home, when I queried his behaviour he said, 'Mum, did you have to dress up like a rainbow? Everyone's staring.' I looked down at my leopard-print jeans, purple and gold t-shirt, diamante necklace and high-heeled orange boots and smiled broadly.

'Yes I did and aren't you lucky?!'

Fortunately, Marco wasn't born a few years earlier when I was getting dressed at my childhood friend Fiona's house for her thirtieth birthday party. The doorbell rang and in a state of panic Fiona looked me up and down from head-to-toe.

'Quick,' she said, 'put on your skirt! My guests are arriving.' She laughed with shocked surprise when I told her my skirt was already on. It just happened to be rather short!

Marco is not the only one who does not approve of my unique sense of style. I have often felt the stares of people when I walk into a room or stroll down a street. In Barcelona I blended right in! I am certain my father, whoever he was, would have been proud of my newly purchased dress from the Barcelonian designer Surkana, figure-hugging cotton fabric, covered in large swirls of yellow, red, pink, blue and green.

Weaving through the maze of streets with Marco and Jack, it was hard not to feel my father's presence everywhere. As we passed many men in their sixties, I found myself staring at each one thinking, 'Perhaps he's the one?' 'I wonder if it's him.' 'Him, yes, could it be him?'

Sadly, even if there had been a striking resemblance and I had wanted to stop and ask if he'd had an affair with a beautiful English girl in 1965, I wouldn't have been able to. The only Spanish word I knew was 'Hola'. I needed help.

That's when I remembered what Nicolas had said just before he waved us off at the train station. You remember Nicolas from Alet, our friend who loathed cheese and slow drivers, but who singlehandedly ensured I stayed in touch with Luc during the four weeks I was in Alet? Well, on discovering we were going to Barcelona, he told us if we had an emergency we could ring his friends Cecelia and Oscar, who lived in Barcelona.

As you can probably guess, I wasn't waiting for any emergency. On our arrival I ran down to the nearest pay phone and rang them immediately. I introduced myself as 'Nicolas's good friend Rebekah,' and asked if they could spare time for a coffee.

Cecelia and Oscar arrived two hours later.

Even though they were Spanish, they both spoke perfect English. They were in their forties and, like me, had met and become good friends with Nicolas during a holiday in Alet. When they offered to drive us to Park Güell, we eagerly accepted.

It was fascinating to be introduced to the work of Spain's most famous architect, Antoni Gaudi. Oscar was a teacher of photography with a keen eye for Gaudi's work and who shared his love of beauty with the inmates of a local prison where he worked. Perhaps he encouraged them to focus on the beauty in small things now that they were denied access to the larger world. His eye for detail encouraged Marco to appreciate Gaudi's work too. So, instead of rushing past objects of art as he had done in Paris, he listened attentively to Oscar's running commentary about the intricate detail of Gaudi's mosaics.

Jack was especially fond of the mosaic-dragon fountain at the entrance of the park and he forced his way through the crowd of other tourists so he could climb onto it. For me, it was the park bench near the entrance, which Oscar said was the longest continuous park bench in the world, which impressed me most. It was built in the form of a sea serpent and decorated with multi-hued mosaics. Gaudi took inspiration from an impression left by the buttocks of a naked workman in wet clay. I was happy to make use of it. My bottom was a perfect fit.

After a beautiful Sunday morning walking around the park, our new friends treated us to lunch at their favourite local *tapas* bar, La Esquinica. After waiting half an hour for a table we gorged ourselves on morsels of caramelised pork, melt-in-your-mouth calamari – the best I have ever tasted, and *bravas*, a spicy potato dish which Marco, Jack and I literally fought over. The restaurant was far away from the tourist area of

Barcelona, so it was frequented by locals, many of whom were elderly. It was thought provoking to watch these characters dining and laughing together, celebrating life.

Seeing these elderly people enjoying themselves made me recall the time during my flight attendant days, when Nanny spent Christmas in a rest home because I was working overseas. My neighbour Lorraine had left in tears after a visit with her on Christmas Day. Lorraine later told me for the Christmas meal Nanny had been served a plate of cold peas, one boiled potato and a cold chicken drumstick. If that was Christmas food, it horrified me to imagine what a regular meal was like. Nanny was appalled too. She might have been ninety-three when she died, but she enjoyed good food until the end of her days. Two weeks before her death I took her to Sitting Duck, her favourite café, located at Auckland's Westhaven Marina. She ordered a full English breakfast of two poached eggs, two pieces of multi-grain toast, three rashers of crispy bacon, two grilled tomatoes and one breakfast sausage. Although it took her one hour and twelve minutes to clear the plate, she ate every morsel. She would have loved Oscar and Cecelia's *tapas* bar.

As Oscar and Cecelia talked to Marco and Jack about Oscar's obsession with table soccer I continued to enjoy watching the older folk relishing their gourmet delights. One such elderly man dining alone was dressed in a suit and tie. How I wished I had the time and language to find out his life story. Would my own paternal grandfather have dressed so smartly and been a lover of good food too?

It was here I told Oscar about my mother and the mystery of my father. I opened my handbag and opened the small packet that held my mother's letters. Oscar stopped eating and read each letter with a serious expression.

'What else do you know about your father?' he asked.

'Nothing,' I replied.

Oscar studied the letters once more, and noticing the address on the top of each one said, 'Perhaps you can come back to Spain alone one day when you have more time. I have cousins in San Sebastian, so we could try to locate the family she stayed with there. They might know something about the young men she met.'

'Oh, I would love to,' I whispered, trying not to let the boys hear, knowing they would beg to come back too. Such a pilgrimage would be much easier to take alone.

When Oscar and Cecelia dropped us back at our apartment later that day, Marco asked if he could go home with them and stay for the night. They generously agreed to his request and returned him to me not one but two days later. Apparently when Marco left in their car he instantly exclaimed with a sigh of relief, 'Yippee, no Jack!'

I found it extraordinary that Oscar and Ceclia were so eager to give us their time and affection, considering we had only just met that very day. I have to say I agree with the great Irish poet William Butler Yeats, 'There are no strangers here; only friends you haven't yet met.'

I was pleasantly surprised that Barcelona, like Paris, was a child-friendly city. Nearly every street corner revealed another playground for the kids. The local playgrounds abounded with young children, many of whom were accompanied by their grandparents. Cecelia told me this was because in most cases the childrens' parents were working. I would certainly have preferred my father or mother to look after Marco and Jack, instead of their spending hours in day-care while I was working.

The most memorable visit to a Spanish playground occurred during our fourth day of sightseeing. The boys swung and climbed on the jungle gym while a group of sixty-year-old men played *boules* beside them. I was drawn to one of the men, who wore an orange-and-purple-striped jumper, red trousers and turquoise shoes and spent the entire time laughing loudly and jumping up in the air, cheering each time he scored. I imagined him recognising me as his long, lost daughter and approaching the boys and me to embrace us. He was my kind of dad.

As I was dreaming of happy families I noticed a mouse dart across the grass. I quickly alerted Marco and Jack, knowing they would love to see this little wild creature, which ran near the group playing *boules*. Even though the men looked up and saw the boys following the mouse, my imaginary dad violently stomped on the rodent's head, then picked up the mutilated body with a piece of old newspaper and tossed it into a nearby rubbish bin. It was a rather cruel end to my father fantasy.

The evening before our departure to the French Riviera, Marco, Jack and I met Oscar at a lake for a boat ride. As I sat beside Oscar rowing us in the setting sun, I imagined my father in his place. Rowing the little wooden boat, my father would softly tell me the story about the beautiful long haired, brown-eyed English girl he had met forty-two years ago.

PART 8
French Riviera

Chapter 16

Nine years ago, I sat at my Auntie Doris's Formica kitchen table as she bustled around in the kitchen preparing a hearty lentil soup for lunch. Four-month-old Marco napped in the spare bedroom. Doris and I were not talking. I was still seething from an argument we had earlier that morning.

I had flown to England eight weeks earlier with four-month-old Marco to be closer to Marco's father, Stephan, who was working in West Africa. I had spent thirty horrible hours trying to keep my crying baby from disturbing the sleeping passengers. I planned to stay with Auntie Doris for two months and visit Paris for the occasional weekend to meet Stephan so he could spend time with his newborn son and me. The other forty-plus days I had to live with an eighty-two-year-old, who had never had children yet had strong opinions about how they should be raised.

I tried to be tolerant when Doris criticised my parenting with regular comments such as, 'The baby is not dressed properly.' 'Have you fed him enough?' 'You shouldn't take a baby out in the cold air.' After weeks of this constant disapproval, I broke down. When she said, 'Rebekah, you should not use disposable nappies. You should use cloth ones like my mother did,' I snapped. I dropped to the floor, lay on my back with legs and arms flailing in the air and screamed. Then I stormed out of the room, slamming the door behind me – baby and aunt left speechless in my wake.

The soup still had twenty minutes to simmer before it would be ready. Doris sat down at the table with me, took my hand and said, 'Let's not fight.'

Although her opinions were hard to swallow, she had opened her home to Marco and me. This was probably very difficult for her considering she had lived alone for the previous twenty years.

'I'm sorry,' we said in unison.

Doris opened her handbag and pulled out a brown envelope.

'I've wanted to show you these photos ever since you arrived, but we've never had a quiet moment.'

She handed me the pile.

'This is where Uncle Jack and I had our honeymoon.'

I looked at the black-and-white photographs: small hotels dotted along the seafront, deserted cobblestone streets, a beautiful cliff-top garden burgeoning with cacti, swimmers frolicking in the calm sea. I watched Doris as she described memory after memory. The frown lines on her face softened as she told me her time with Uncle Jack in Villefranche, a small town situated in the French Riviera between Nice and Monaco, 'was the best week of my life.'

Ten years later, I caught an Air Canada flight from London to Montreal after Doris's funeral. I struggled to stretch my legs, but it was impossible in such a tiny space. There was no way I was going to sleep sitting upright. I had a copy of Leonard Cohen's *The Favourite Game* and while rummaging through my handbag to find it, re-discovered the brown envelope my cousin had given me from Doris's belongings, tucked deep inside a small pocket. While carefully studying the black-and-white photographs of Doris and Jack, hand-in-hand in the French Riviera I decided I would take the boys on a honeymoon.

I rented an apartment in Villefranche from Ian, an Englishman married to a beautiful French woman named Lise-Marie. He emailed me before our departure from Barcelona to inform me he could get us discounted plane tickets that would enable us to travel to Nice in just one hour. However, because I still considered train travel to be more romantic, especially after my encounter with Luc in Canada, I turned down Ian's kind offer. Little did I realise our 'romantic adventure' would entail a twelve-hour trip on four different trains. This meant shifting ten pieces of luggage plus a sleeping toddler up and down numerous sets of stairs four times from platform one to platform seven. Each time we crossed platforms I would have to walk backwards so I could keep Jack, who was asleep in his stroller in my line of vision on platform one. After dumping a set of cases on platform seven we returned to platform one and Marco had to walk backwards to keep his eye on the cases left behind. After repeating this process four times our calf muscles were burning and my heart was throbbing, due to the fear I felt knowing that any moment a high-speed train could fly through the station and possibly soar Jack's stroller off the platform with the intense gust of wind its motion created.

If I thought train travel in Canada had been difficult, this was horrendous in comparison. How deluded I was to have turned down those discounted plane tickets.

When an observant passenger later commented on Marco's helpful nature, I agreed. 'Yes, he's amazing. He is always such a great help to me and he never complains.'

Overhearing our conversation, Marco interjected, 'Actually Mum, I do complain. I just mumble under my breath.'

Being the son of a single mum often placed Marco in situations most children wouldn't experience. Most often this meant doing simple things like helping me lift heavy objects, or looking after his little brother. Then there were the more demanding requests, like assisting me in my quest to find love. Once I entered a competition to win a date with Ellen DeGeneres' disc jockey Tony. After laminating four life-size headshots of the British-born Nigerian, I asked Marco to take photos of the four Tonys and me in various locations. Reluctantly, he snapped shots of us in bed (in my nightie), at the beach, on top of a mountain, in a cafe and in the supermarket. However, when I called Marco into the bathroom to take photos of the laminated Tony (complete with shower cap) and me peeking out from behind the shower curtain (in a bikini) he began to protest. In spite of that he did it because out of sheer loyalty Marco would do anything for me, regardless of his childlike embarrassment.

Ellen didn't pick me to be Tony's date. Instead, she chose a skinny, young, pretty girl. Perhaps it had something to do with my response to Ellen's question, 'What are you allergic to?' I hoped my answer, 'Men who show the rim of their toupee, have false teeth, have nervous sweat issues or are Nigerian romance scammers,' would have made her laugh, but that was before I discovered Tony was Nigerian! However, I still think it was a better answer than the winner's, who said, 'Onions!'

Exhausted after our numerous platform changes and train journey, it was a great relief to find Ian and his wife Lise-Marie waiting for us at the station with their brand new Mercedes-Benz C-Class to deliver us to the apartment. I suspect Ian may have regretted offering to pick us up when the plastic boot liner cracked pushing in the last case, but there was no visible hesitation as we stood there, surrounded by baggage, too tired to take another step.

On our arrival at Villefranche I instantly recognised the waterfront lined with hotels from Doris's photo. Like so many of the small villages we had visited in France, this one had not changed in sixty years and I imagined Doris arriving in this very place all those years ago. I saw her in her twin set, sensible shoes, tights and perfectly-set hair on the arm of the man she adored.

We followed Ian along the cobblestone streets, weaving our way through tunnels and a labyrinth of narrow lanes. Cars were banned on the road so we were able to move freely with our suitcases. Arriving at the door of the apartment, Ian stopped and I wondered if he had forgotten the key. When he opened the door I understood the hesitation and horror in his face.

Stairs!

No ordinary stairs.

Completely and entirely vertical stairs.

Sweat dripped off his brow as he lugged each piece up to our third-floor apartment – a total of ten trips. Our fitness levels would obviously increase during our two-week stay here. Another advantage of our elevated apartment was its panoramic view. Our living room window overlooked the harbour and each morning I opened the shutters to see what new twenty million dollar yacht had arrived overnight.

Our window also looked directly onto another apartment. Every day I nodded politely to my neighbour, an elderly woman whom I saw frequently on her balcony watching those walking past below her. She reminded me of Nanny and Doris, women from a generation now gone. I wondered if this old lady had a granddaughter or great-niece who would one day regret not asking questions about her past. Questions similar to my own about Nanny, such as who were the handsome men surrounding her in a photograph, or were there any lovers in her life after her husband left her for another woman thirty years younger than himself? Questions similar to mine about Doris, like why did she never have children of her own? Did she find it hard to maintain relationships with people as a result of spending months in an isolation ward when she was three years old and suffering from diphtheria?

Ian and Lise-Marie invited us for dinner at their beautiful home in the nearby village of Èze the following night. Their house was surrounded by lush, tropical vegetation and overlooked the sparkling Mediterranean. We dined outdoors enjoying the balmy evening and delighting in the chorus of toads which had taken refuge in an absent neighbour's swimming pool.

Ian's generosity continued when he offered to take Marco sailing on his yacht the following day. I tried not to feel too envious as I watched him sail into the distance while I remained on the marina with a three-year-old screaming for ice cream.

Our visit to Èze with Ian and Lise-Marie left me curious to explore this picturesque mountain village we had viewed only briefly on the way to their house. I was also keen to visit Jardin d'Èze, otherwise known as the Exotic Garden, since it featured in one of Doris's honeymoon photos.

This garden was perched on a cliff top 427 metres high. Two days later we took a bus up the steep winding road to the top of the mountain and walked into a garden filled with exotic cacti and sculptures. It was there I decided to capture all the places displayed in Doris's photos with my own camera. I hoped to create an heirloom to pass on to the boys, as a connection to Doris whom they never really knew. When I'd received the news in Montreal that Doris was dead, I hadn't been ready to lose her. I still wasn't.

It took an hour before I found the spot in the garden which was closest to the image in my hand. It was perfect. The boys and I then ate ham and cheese baguettes and sat quietly enjoying the panoramic view. As we ate, I felt Doris sitting beside us.

During our time in the French Riviera we took a few day trips to Monte Carlo, Monaco. Spending the day there with two young children was hardly the sophisticated experience I had imagined. I did not dress in a blue chiffon dress with golden, glittery shoes and visit the Monte Carlo Casino as Doris had. Nevertheless, a fabulous afternoon exploring the Musée Océanographique (Oceanographic Museum) and Aquarium, helped to compensate.

Despite the glorious bird's-eye-view of the city below the museum, I was glad Doris was not there that day. While she would have loved the vista, her severe claustrophobia may have brought on a panic attack. We had to battle hoards of elderly tourists who forced their way into the museum's elevator. Regardless of their age, I was not going to be shoved out of the way, so Marco, Jack and I joined forces and stood our ground in the miniscule space.

Doris would not have been able to bear the elevator and she would have hated the trains even more. Hundreds of cruise ship passengers lined the platform waiting to board our train back to Villefranche where their ship was departing in one hour. As they surged into the carriage I yelled, 'You're smothering my baby!' but my plea had no effect on these tourists desperate not to miss their ship. When Marco and I vehemently elbowed these aggressive pensioners in the ribs there was still no response. Immune to any sense of courtesy they continued to push, shove and knock all three of us, left and right. Marco and I eyed each other, raised our brows and began our defensive elbow attack again, this time with greater force and some pleasure.

Our day trips to Monaco stunned Marco. He could not get over the way the children dressed and pointed out children wearing designer clothing, complete with colour-coordinated belts and shoes, on sweltering summer days. As for my appearance every day in Monaco, I could imagine Doris's disapproval of my Kiwi-farmer black shorts and singlet.

When I visited Doris during my flight attendant days I would catch the train from Heathrow to the small village of East Horsley, Surrey and it became a tradition to have a lamb stew lunch at the local golf course restaurant the following day. Travelling light, I would only bring skin-tight leggings and tight-fitting t-shirts. Doris was horrified by this attire and insisted I wear a 'sensible skirt'. So off we went, arm in arm, in matching below-the-knee woollen beige skirts. She was jubilant while I felt humiliated. At least she didn't insist I wear a pair of her knee-length bloomers underneath.

While I might not have been as stylish as Doris was in Monaco, I know I was much more comfortable.

The fifth of June in Villefranche was a Thursday. The sky was a sapphire blue and the sun shone intensely. I smiled as Jack and Marco rushed to wish me happy birthday. Two years before, I'd cancelled my fortieth birthday party because Nanny had died and I was so grief stricken I was unable to get out of bed. This fifth day of June I felt happy and excited.

My forty-second birthday in Villefranche began with an early morning walk to the local *pâtisserie* where Marco, Jack and I filled a box with chocolate éclairs, meringues, macaroons and brioche. These were eaten back at our apartment with coffee and juice whilst looking out over the sparkling ocean.

After this feast we headed to a nearby beach early enough to secure a spot for our towels. From mid-morning onwards, large crowds moved in. Men and women of all ages strutted about in their G-string bikini bottoms, which unfortunately included many male pensioners we had already encountered in Monaco. It was not an attractive sight, but made me content to be single for the meantime.

We celebrated my birthday dinner at a Vietnamese restaurant called Mekong. In spite of complimentary birthday cocktails, the meal did not go as I hoped. Marco sat with arms crossed and refused to talk after discovering his choice of spare ribs was sold out. When he began to cry I hauled him out of the restaurant by his shirt collar, took some deep breaths and told him to behave.

'You're dining in the French Riviera while most of your friends are eating the same old meat and three veg at home.'

Fortunately, this was enough to change his mind and back inside he enjoyed a delicious Vietnamese chicken curry.

Perhaps to make up for this incident, Marco offered to take Jack back to the apartment after our main course to give me a little time alone. I relaxed in my chair and took a deep breath for the first time all evening. This rare feeling of freedom was made perfect by the restaurant's complimentary banana fritters, a glass of Mekhong whiskey and a singing waiter.

As I raised my glass to Doris and sipped the warm liquid, I caught sight of my cat-suit attire reflected in the window. I was sure I saw Doris's face frowning in the frame. Happy Birthday to me!

PART 9

Italy

Chapter 17

'I'm not moving!' Marco protested as he sat down on Vernazza's cobblestone pavement, surrounded by black, red, green and blue suitcases, a pushchair, three carry-on bags and the black shopping trolley I had bought in Barcelona.

We were lost.

After four long and exhausting train rides from Villefranche, we had finally reached our first Italian destination. Unable to find the apartment I'd rented we had walked around in circles for nearly an hour. Sweat was dripping off our already grimy bodies and it was sweltering, even though it was almost five o'clock. When we asked a group of elderly ladies sitting on a bench for directions, speaking only Italian, one woman clutching a pink handkerchief pointed left in the direction of the sea. Another lady with a hooknose shook her head and pointed another way. Then they began to argue loudly, so we slunk away before a fight broke out.

At last, and entirely by chance, we came across the address in my notebook. The place was incredible. A studio on the second floor of an old stone apartment building, it looked over the piazza and the surrounding harbour. I hurried the boys to bed and leaving the unpacking until the morning, slumped into a soft armchair with a Bellini cocktail and began to soak up the setting sun shimmering its golden light onto the harbour below.

I could see elderly ladies in colourful florals and heels, walking arm in arm in the streets or sitting in groups on wooden benches, four or five to a bench, noisily chatting together or watching the world go by. Arguments about directions were long forgotten!

Vernazza was part of Cinque Terre, a national park connecting the five coastal villages of the region: Vernazza, Corniglia, Manarola, Riomaggiore and Monterosso al Mare. Each of the villages – originally medieval fishing settlements – was perched on rocky pinnacles among hilly olive groves and vineyards, which until very recently could only be accessed by boat or train. During our stay in Vernazza we were surprised to learn that cars were still not allowed in the villages.

We spent five days in Cinque Terre and each day we walked a different trail. Hiking the four cliff-top footpaths linking the villages meant we had to negotiate an extremely narrow rocky shoreline – not an easy task with a three-year-old. Hearing that a gigantic rogue wave had claimed the life of a young American woman the previous year on the path to Manarola from Corniglia increased my anxiety about safety.

A less treacherous walk was called Via dell'Amore, a coastal path overlooking the ocean and surrounded by huge rock formations, leading from the village of Manarola to Riomaggiore. Translated, Via dell'Amore means 'Love Walk' and was so-named because along the trail you pass through the 'tunnel of love' which is a small concrete tunnel, smothered with thousands of graffiti messages of love, as far back as the 1930s. Marco and Jack added to the collection engraving the words, 'We love Mum' with a sharp rock Marco found nearby. The simple pleasure of being in such a beautiful place with my boys made me very happy.

After every walk we rewarded ourselves with large meals of

spaghetti marinara – fresh pasta topped with a huge pile of prawns, scallops, mussels, calamari and red mullet.

All the local restaurants served the freshest food, but the Posada eatery in Corniglia had the added advantage of being elevated and therefore overlooked the glistening Mediterranean. Seating was outdoors and surrounded by a tropical garden. Famished and out of breath after climbing no less that 368 stairs, we collapsed at a table and beckoned a waiter, ordering a plate of pasta, as fast as the chef could cook it.

However, no meal with my boys was ever just a meal. Shortly after finishing his bowl of spaghetti bolognaise, the ever-affectionate Jack, his mouth covered in red pasta sauce, asked our waiter, Vincenzo, for a kiss. After planting a kiss on Jack's head, Vincenzo declared it was now time for him to kiss Jack's mama! Even though he wasn't very attractive – skinny and unshaven with beady eyes – it was three years since I had last been kissed, so I certainly was not about to protest. Besides, I decided it wouldn't hurt to get in a little practise. Little did I know that working in the same eatery was Vincenzo's girlfriend, who had witnessed the entire episode. Vincenzo was last seen running from the kitchen with his girlfriend, brandishing a wooden rolling pin, in hot pursuit.

The kiss with the Italian waiter gave me courage to wear a new red-and-yellow-striped bikini I had purchased on our last day in the French Riviera. I couldn't wait to put it on. Manarola's deep green lagoon was the perfect place for a swim after the tiring three hour walk from Corniglia. Jack had hiked the whole way in the heat without complaint, thanks to Marco's jokes and songs. Meanwhile, I sailed along the path enjoying the view of the Mediterranean and dreaming of walks like this in the arms of a lover and without kids.

As soon as we reached the water's edge, both boys were eager to jump in and join a large group of school kids who were also cooling off.

Marco snorkeled with a rented mask, chasing the myriad of fish, yelling as he came up for air, 'Mum, I saw a crab.' Meanwhile, I hung onto Jack from a metal ladder as he kept struggling to join Marco. It was only when he saw something move near the ladder he stopped thrashing about. Something big was down there, it was a giant orange octopus! Lunging out of the water in panic, I couldn't steady myself and kept slipping back. Quickly I pushed Jack out and then pulled myself up trying to breathe and shout at Marco at the same time. Sensing my urgency Marco threw off his mask and swam towards me as fast as he could.

The commotion drew a crowd, including an elderly Italian man who had been watching. Suddenly and unexpectedly he took off his belt and shoved it towards Marco, who had also jumped out of the water. I jerked Marco away from the stranger, but the old guy didn't give up and encouraged Marco to hold his belt in the water. This enticed the octopus to cling onto it, so the creature could be pulled out of the water.

Initially, I admired this man who wasn't a weirdo after all. Maybe he was a science teacher wanting to give the large group of children gathering around, a closer look. However, after our Barcelonean mouse experience I should have known better. Could you believe it? There, in front of the curious children, the man grabbed the octopus, twisted its body inside out, and then walked off with the creature. Dinner?

A group of construction workers nearby had also noticed the catch. As soon as the old man left they came over and offered Marco fifty euros to dive down for another octopus. Marco refused. I like fresh seafood as much as the next person, but to see such a beautiful animal removed so violently from its natural habitat horrified me. I prefer mine vacuum packed, thanks.

'Don't leave without me!' cried a female passenger sitting opposite us, as we arrived at Rome's Termini train station from the Cinque Terre. 'Grab my hand as we leave the train and don't let go until I get you into a taxi.' Holding the boys' hands tightly, the concerned stranger walked us to a waiting taxi and waved us off with a relieved smile.

This dramatic arrival was the first time since leaving New Zealand that I had felt intimidated by our surroundings. However, it made an exciting change from the relaxed pace of life we had been experiencing in Cinque Terre and southern France. In just two months our trip would be over, but had I really experienced the adventure I had been longing for before we left? I still felt there was unfinished business including bigger, tougher challenges. Everything until now had been sightseeing, restaurant eating and top-quality accommodation. Perhaps the Europe I had experienced was too familiar, too predictable?

Rome, on the other hand, had a reputation as an edgy city. My *Let's Go Italy* guidebook stated, 'In order to avoid a night time Gypsy-mugging, plan your Termini route beforehand.' As our train pulled into Termini, I had conflicting feelings of fear and excitement. Most of all I anticipated adventure.

Once inside our taxi my excitement turned to dread. The driver spoke little English and kept glaring at me whilst speaking Italian with an abrasive tone. I had no idea what he was saying. Suddenly he pulled over at a bus stop and tried to speak in English.

'We stop now. You change taxis. We wait.'

I glanced at Marco, who looked rather pale and smiled, in an attempt to reassure him. Deep down my stomach was churning. My imagination took flight and I began to sweat with anxiety. Was this driver part of some gang about to abduct us and sell us into slavery, or worse? I leaned over towards Marco and whispered, 'If I start having a coughing fit, that's the signal to jump out of the taxi and run.' Marco looked at me as if I was mad, but he knew by the serious look on my face I meant business. Five more minutes passed before the driver mumbled something in Italian and took off again. No gang members. No people smugglers. I was slightly disappointed. Instead, we arrived safely at my Auntie Jill's. She stood in the doorway of her apartment in a Laura Ashley dress and asked, 'Would you like a nice hot cup of tea?'

'No,' I replied firmly.

I didn't want a cup of tea. I was in Italy. I wanted excitement. Yet I had chosen to stay with my elderly British aunt, so perhaps I shouldn't have expected anything different.

We were staying with Jill for ten days (a shock for my mother's seventy-nine year old cousin, who through a misunderstanding thought we were coming for four).

Jill had left England fifty years earlier, met an Italian doctor and settled in Rome. There, she worked for Radio Vatican and raised her three children, Michele, Luca and Prisca. Marco flinched when I warned the boys to be on their best behaviour.

'Remember,' I said, 'Jill works for the Pope!' Jack on the other hand didn't give a toss.

When I finally accepted the cup of tea, Jill sat down and handed me a poem she had written. It was about my mother. She had entitled it, *An Elegy for my Cousin*. The poem was precious to me, because very few people had spoken of my mother since her death. Now that Nanny and Doris had gone, there were only a handful of relatives left who remembered her but even they didn't talk about her often. My mother's brother, my uncle who had convinced Nanny to bring me to New Zealand where he still lived, had seldom spoken about her, which I found frustrating because I wanted to know so much more than Nanny had told me. I like to think the indifference I observed was not indifference at all – just grief over the loss of his younger sister when he was in his early twenties.

Consequently, meeting Jill was the opportunity I had longed for as a young girl to learn about my mother. Did she play with dolls, or was she more of a tomboy like me? Had the agoraphobia she suffered struck when she was a child, and as a young woman how did she feel when she became pregnant with me? Was she devastated that her dream of attending university was shattered? Most importantly, did my mother know she was going to die? If so, how did she feel about leaving her four-year-old child? Had she confided in her cousin? I hadn't bothered to ask Jill these questions when I had met her in Rome twenty years earlier. Now that Doris and Nanny were dead she was my last hope. Everybody else had been quizzed.

Then I read the opening lines of Jill's poem. '*You are dead. And I did not even know you. You lived. A stranger, for we hardly met . . . And I do not even know what you looked like. A slim form, a gentle face, a cool smile – Is that too far from the truth?*

There was no one else left.

My questions were going to remain unanswered.

Why did I leave it so long?

Why didn't anyone think to tell me about her?

My mother it seemed, was going to remain enigmatic forever.

After placing the poem safely in my handbag I asked Jill about Monte Sergio, the suburb where she lived. Being a huge fan of *The Sopranos*, I was eager to explore her neighbourhood, which in a letter she had written, 'was heavily controlled by the Mafia.'

'One Christmas Eve,' Jill said, 'I received a call from my neighbour warning me that my apartment's windows had been blown out by a bomb planted by the Mafia. They had wanted to destroy a bar on the ground floor of my building as payback for its owner's overdue debts.' When Jill told me her local grocery store was also under the Mafia's control I swiftly dragged the boys there hoping to see some action.

Once inside the dark grocery the first thing I noticed was not mobsters but walls lined floor-to-ceiling with boxes of dried spaghetti, penne, lasagna, fettuccine, fusilli and macaroni pasta – a foodie's paradise. I had never before seen so many different varieties of pasta. Looking down the aisles to the back of the store, I saw no shady characters lurking amongst the boxes of dried lasagna. Instead, the proprietor Marcello and his son Luigi greeted us immediately with deep hugs and a rush of words in Italian. The only words I could contribute to the conversation were *ciao* and *grazie*, but they didn't seem to notice. In spite of my lack of understanding, I loved listening to the musical intonation of the words as they spoke. Each time we visited I felt as if I was stepping into a live opera performance rather than a small food store on the corner of a busy suburban street. Such loud and animated surroundings made me feel energized and it was a sharp contrast to the large supermarkets I had traditionally frequented, where the only words uttered by the exhausted and underpaid checkout operators were, 'Paper or plastic?'

Failing to find any Mafia action at Jill's grocer, I decided to make regular visits to the Piazza Guadalupe, a busy square below Jill's home, overflowing with residents from neighbouring apartments who gathered there to talk and play. Each morning, I sat in the square listening to them chatting on the wooden benches lining the periphery. The seats facing inwards encouraged them to wave and call out to each other from across the square, creating a real sense of community. While the adults chatted, the children, including Marco and Jack, frolicked in the water from the fountains.

Everyone was friendly – no gangsters anywhere. However, I did encounter an outspoken matriarch on one occasion. The boys had just licked the last remains of lemon gelato from their cones, when without any introduction, a middle-aged woman turned to Marco and said in heavily Italian-accented English, 'Young man, my three sons all desert me.'

Marco's uncomfortable grimace did not deter her from continuing.

'They met their wives ten years ago and left me miserable. They never come and see me, or look after me anymore. I did everything for them.'

Marco was speechless. He looked at me. I shrugged. He looked at his feet and began fiddling with his shoelace. The woman continued.

'You must never do this to your mother. You must always look after her when you are a man.'

Marco smiled sweetly in response.

I grinned.

I think this woman's demands may have sunk in because after our return to New Zealand I found a note hidden in Marco's underwear drawer he had written to himself, 'Take mum to stay at the Ritz, Paris, when she's old.' Now, that's my boy! He had obviously taken note of my sense of disappointment and embarrassment when we had walked into the hotel intending on having a pizza, but left immediately and unfed after discovering it was going to cost fifty euros!

Anyway, I'm glad we couldn't afford to eat at the Ritz that day, because I think even a renowned hotel such as the Ritz would have found it hard to compete with the the smell of pizza that drifted past me as I sat in the piazza below Jill's apartment a few weeks later. Although I was unable to understand most of the conversations I overheard in the piazza, I was content just to sit and watch. Most of the young men dressed as if they had just walked off the set of *The Godfather* and the women were wrapped in skin-tight clothing with gold jewellery enhancing their richly-tanned bodies. One elderly man I noticed sitting alone was wearing a blue-and-white pinstriped shirt, black trousers, red waistcoat, white bowtie and black-and-white brogue shoes. Fantastic!

The emphasis on fashion in Rome was evident everywhere. I was amused when I saw a woman at Rome's Bioparco pushing a pram wearing black stilettos, very short black shorts and a black leather and lace top. What a contrast this was from most Kiwi mums in their tracksuits and trainers at the zoo.

When planning our itinerary originally, Marco had asked if we could go to Rome.

'Can we visit the Colosseum?' he asked. 'Mr Tilby at school said that's where the gladiators fought in ancient Rome.'

I agreed.

However, by the time we reached Rome we had been away for six months, which amounted to twenty-four weeks of sightseeing, visiting one iconic monument and statue after another. Jack and I were tired. Still, I knew Marco would get significantly more pleasure visiting the Colosseum, than reading about it in a school textbook.

Neither Marco nor I were disappointed. After walking through its echoing chambers we both stood breathless next to the massive stone columns and arches looming above us. This state of wonder was interrupted by hoards of tourists who pushed past us and I wished their guide's irritating shouting voices could be silenced by the sound of racing chariots.

Marco seemed unaffected by the crowds. He was fixated.

'Mum!' he said, reading from his guide, 'This place once held up to 50,000 fanatical spectators who, during the first 100 days of its opening in 80 AD, had watched 5,000 wild beasts perish.'

How awful, I thought.

'How cool!' he declared. 'I wish I could have been there!'

I thought about giving Marco a lecture on the mistreatment of animals, but then I remembered he was a spellbound ten-year-old. Sermons could wait.

Seeing Marco's wonder reminded me of the thrill I felt twenty years earlier, on my first visit during my flying years. At that time it was all about the adventure and fun when my cousin Michele, Jill's son, and his friends took me to the Colosseum after dark. At midnight we climbed over the huge entrance gates and crawled on our hands and knees along the high stonewalls, bruising and scraping our legs, and played hide and seek in the old lion pits with other locals who had also crept in. A group of young Italian men and women sat playing guitars and drinking under a huge concrete column and though I noticed many security guards on duty, they appeared to turn a blind eye to the antics.

Although my return visit to the Colosseum with the boys didn't involve a midnight rendezvous and rolling in lion pits, it was not without incident. Jill suggested that before leaving I take photos of the boys with the men dressed up as Roman soldiers who stand outside the Colosseum. After Marco chose the soldiers he wanted to be photographed with I asked one of them how much he wanted for the photo.

'*Madame*, a donation would be appreciated,' he replied.

After fifty or sixty photos I pulled out five euros and handed it to the soldier. Without looking at it, he shoved it back to me and shouted, 'We want at least ten euros!'

'Excuse me, but you asked for a donation,' I replied, handing him the five euros again, but feeling very intimidated. As Marco was looking at the pictures on my camera, one of the soldiers grabbed the camera and insisted we delete them. By this stage Marco was trembling.

'Don't worry,' I whispered. 'Delete the photos! I took photos on your camera too. They obviously didn't notice.'

Even after I erased the photos the soldier came within a few inches of my face and shouted, 'Bitch!'

Though part of me wanted to respond, I decided to err on the side of safety. After all, these soldiers were armed with authentic swords! So, I grabbed the boys and we did a runner. An adventure – finally!

The Roman soldier fiasco certainly increased our adrenalin levels, but it was only momentary. Rome just wasn't the same thrill I'd experienced twenty years ago. I guess that's what happens when you throw two kids in the mix! Nevertheless, we visited the Trevi Fountain, Sistine Chapel, Spanish Steps and Saint Peter's Basilica. Unlike Paris and Barcelona, Rome had few playgrounds where the boys could play in between our sightseeing. Apparently whenever these playgrounds were planned excavators often discovered historic ruins beneath the proposed site. I suppose this attitude towards the city's history should be admired, but try making a frustrated three-year-old understand that!

The summer heat also stifled our enjoyment of Rome's sights. Each day we returned black with dirt from the city's pollution and exhausted from walking in the blistering heat. In addition, thousands of other tourists elbowed, pushed and jostled us as we tried to see as much as we could.

By this stage I was rapidly tiring of historic monuments and attractions and although my love of Italy was still intact, the spontaneity and excitement I felt leaving New Zealand was fading. More memorable were the hours upon hours spent waiting in queues, dodging other tired, hungry and impatient tourists. Was I over our European holiday?

I had been longing to visit Cacio e Pepe, a highly-rated eatery, during our stay in Rome, but it seemed like just another restaurant, with yet another meal saturated in too much olive oil. This feeling of indifference, even annoyance, was aggravated by a woman from Hong Kong at the table next to us with seven members of her family.

'What are those little things on your plate?' she inquired, moving her chair closer and pointing to my lunch. Before I had time to respond, she had helped herself to the homemade ravioli on my plate.

'Oh, that's delicious,' she declared to everyone.

I was livid.

Just as the woman was about to dig her fork into my plate of fresh anchovies, Jack dropped the glass of lemonade he was holding. It flew into the air, smashing on the floor beside her. Apparently a small shard of glass scraped her leg, cutting it superficially.

'Oh, I'm so sorry,' I said, in my sweetest, most apologetic voice. 'What a terrible accident.'

While I wasn't sorry at all she had been distracted from her food snatching, I did feel a pang of sympathy over the cut. This quickly disappeared when I noticed her pressing hard on the scratch to squeeze out blood in order to get attention from the restaurant's proprietor, who rushed over and offered her a free gelato. I began to imagine the story she might relate on her return: *Three-year-old Kiwi attacks Chinese woman in Rome with glass.*

As far as I was concerned, she received her just deserts.

Waiting at the bus stop after our far-from-relaxing lunch, a young Italian woman with a pack on her back began chatting to me. She had just returned from a month of trekking around India, where she had ridden on elephants, stayed in palaces and been to a Hindu wedding.

While listening to her, thoughts of London, Paris, Barcelona and Rome faded in a smoky haze. My adventure had been a stroll through a colourful grocery store by comparison. Her journey, on the other hand, had been full of exploration. She had taken risks and gone deep within another culture. How intrepid. How exotic.

Suddenly I realised we were only a month away from returning to New Zealand and all that remained was a stint back in the arms of the Rodrigues' in Montreal, Canada. In spite of looking forward to seeing them again, Canada, like Europe, seemed so familiar, so easy, so unadventurous. Even the promise of excitement in Italy had fallen short. As the backpacker continued talking about pushing her limits in India, I wondered if I had honestly done the same on my trip.

I thought about Christine on the Isle of Wight and how we returned to her when things went sour in the south of England, then how I'd expected Nicolas to come to our rescue when I was homesick for Alet and how we could return to the comfort of Jill's apartment after our Roman soldier encounter. Suddenly I heard Marco yelling.

'Mum! Mum! Get Jack out of the pushchair! It's our bus!'

I saw the bus coming, only a block away.

Then, in the corner of my eye, a red neon sign flashed at me.

It was beckoning.

'Mum, what are you doing? Come on! The bus is here!'

As the Italian backpacker boarded the bus and waved goodbye, I grabbed Marco's arm with one hand and Jack's pushchair with the other and dodged the traffic to get to the other side of the road. I stood staring at the sign hanging in the Quattro Angoli Travel Agency's window which read, 'Discount flights to Vietnam.'

'Mum! What are we doing?'

'We're going on an adventure!'

PART 10

Vietnam

Chapter 18

I could smell adventure in the air as we stepped off the plane in Ho Chi Minh feeling like intrepid travellers at last. Another thirty hours of travelling from Rome with two young boys was just the beginning. Nothing had changed since our long haul flights from New Zealand and Canada, six and seven months earlier, except by now, I'd learned to let go. If Jack threw a Hot Wheels car and hit the head of a businessman three rows in front I'd graciously smile and apologise. If Marco whined incessantly when the airline forgot to order him a kids' meal I would calmly put my headphones on and turn up the volume. The thirty hours were hell for the people sitting around us, but for me, I slept most of the time.

I know I had planned to have more adventure, but I wasn't yet prepared to travel without some form of a safety net. So, before leaving Italy I rang an old friend, Norbert, who lived in the (non-touristy) Binh Tan district to ask if we could stay with him. Nonetheless, as my foot kicked a dead rat on the pavement in front of the gate to his three-storied concrete home, I screamed and realised there was no escaping the intrepid experience after all.

Norbert was an old Swiss friend, once Head Chef at Wellington's Park Royal Hotel where I had worked as a chef twenty years earlier. We became close friends after I returned from my chef's training in London.

Norbert was a quiet, sensible man who hid behind his dense beard and worked tirelessly. He had few friends or family, but loved his Harley Davidson and copious amounts of gourmet food. His large stomach gave him the appearance of a man much older than his twenties.

At that time, my inability to make level-headed decisions regarding men made me a perfect candidate for Norbert's wise concern. Such was the case regarding Pete, my bad-news boyfriend whom I had met earlier during my chef's training in London. You remember, the one with the 'gummy grin' who horrified Auntie Doris? Pete had followed me to New Zealand and had taken hours getting through New Zealand Customs because they discovered a Crocodile Dundee-style hunting knife and a Dominator Pro 40-inch bow with twelve arrows packed in his suitcase.

'These are for hunting,' he casually told the Customs officer. What he left out was the part about me being his target.

Only days after moving temporarily into my bedsit, the once happy-go-lucky man he seemed in England quickly transformed into a controlling and jealous madman. Pete turned out to be a psychopath. I hadn't seen it coming. He went into jealous rages hurling knives in my direction, which pierced the wall centimetres above my head. Pete burned my sheets, smashed my plates and cut my phone lines when he found out I'd gone out one night wearing makeup, without him.

'You're just trying to attract other men,' he would roar, his white English skin turning bright pink with rage.

Soon after his arrival Pete stormed into the hotel during my lunch shift, furious that I had stayed late for staff drinks the previous night. He grabbed me by my apron, dragged me outside and threw me into his Bedford van, driving off at high speed. Hearing me shouting as Pete dragged me outside, Norbert, who had been preoccupied in the office, ran outside and jumped on his Harley, beard flying in the wind, to give chase. Luckily, Norbert was unable to catch up. I am certain if he had, one or the other of them would have ended up dead.

Norbert tried to persuade me to dump Pete after that ordeal, but when Pete begged forgiveness I gave him one last chance. I should have listened to Norbert. Two months later, Pete abducted me again. At seven o'clock one evening while listening to *Prince* on the stereo with Joe, another colleague from work, Pete arrived, breaking down the door with his steel-capped boots and threatening to kill Joe if he didn't, 'Fuck off!'

Without delay Joe sprinted.

I froze.

Pete threw me into his van and drove recklessly up Wellington's Mount Victoria, threatening to drive over the edge when he reached the top. I begged him to take me home. I didn't want to die.

I finally managed to persuade him to drive me home where eight police cars were waiting for him, and the next day Pete was deported back to England.

Later, I knocked on Norbert's door to tell him the good news. He opened a bottle of peach schnapps and we made a toast to friendship and common sense (like doing a runner next time when you discover your boyfriend has no teeth). Then we drank ourselves under the table.

A few months after the abduction incident Norbert told me that, regardless of the stimulation my romantic liaisons had produced, New Zealand was too quiet for him. He decided to continue his cooking career in Vietnam's bustling city of Ho Chi Minh, where he would eventually set up a Swiss-sausage-making factory.

After one failed marriage to a local Vietnamese woman, he moved in with Han. She had straight black hair that fell down to her hips and a beautiful, tall, slim body. Still overweight and nearly fifty, bearded Norbert was doing all right for himself.

A few hours after arriving in Ho Chi Minh we dashed through the streets in a downpour to have dinner at a local restaurant. Although we had been warned to be careful with what we ate, it was hard to be too precious with Norbert as our host. After living in Vietnam for nearly twenty years, Norbert didn't seem to notice the noodle restaurant's brown floodwater flowing all over the broken tiled floor. It was difficult to ignore this as we ate our bowls of pho noodle soup alongside the numerous cockroaches crawling the walls.

It was over dinner that I proudly told Norbert about Luc.

'Who's Luc?'

'I think he might be the one.'

'I hope he's better than that Londoner who almost killed you!'

'Don't worry. Luc's kind, sensitive and admires my independence. He's perfect!'

Feeling a bit queasy after our dinner and jetlagged after the long flight, we returned to Norbert's for an early night. Four hours later both Jack and I woke up and couldn't get back to sleep, so when the sun began to rise we threw on some clothes and headed out for an early morning walk, leaving Marco still sleeping.

I couldn't believe how busy the streets were at five o'clock in the morning. Scooters swamped the road and pots of hot coffee were brewing on red-hot coals by the local street vendors. Men lounged on cushions outside cafes chatting with each other. Later Norbert said, 'That's what many Vietnamese men do all day while the women cook, clean, take care of the children and go to work!'

'Not much different from being a single mum,' I replied.

As Jack and I followed the maze of narrow alleyways we had to dodge the hundreds of scooters whizzing past. Many of the men stopped and offered Jack a ride. These strangers, curious about Jack's red curly locks, looked friendly enough and Jack was keen, but I grabbed his hand and pulled him close while politely declining their offer.

The increased heat from the morning sun made me realise we had been walking the dusty streets for nearly an hour and I felt miles from Norbert's. The overly friendly men who kept stopping to touch Jack made me feel uneasy. I pulled Jack away from another dead rat on the pavement and hurried back to the sanctuary of Norbert's home. The sun was now well up and Han had a platter of fresh guava, jackfruit, litchi and mango waiting for breakfast. We were safe.

It was ironic I felt so secure staying with Norbert and Han, because it was probably the most dangerous part of our visit in Vietnam. This was due to their dog named Lucky.

Marco had spent years wanting a dog, and I had spent years resisting. It's not that I don't like dogs; I'm just not keen on a dog's smell, fur and the thought of cleaning up after it. So, when on the drive back from the airport, Norbert said, 'Hey boys, I hope you're going to help us look after our dog, Lucky,' I winced.

'I want to feed him,' Marco yelled.

'Me too, me too!' added Jack, bouncing on the seat.

The boys' excitement quickly turned to dread when they saw the huge, brown, pit bull terrier, sneering and frothing at the mouth. I cringed and recalled a fourth reason I don't like dogs. They bite.

Each day as we entered or left the house we had to sprint past Lucky's gated bed as fast as possible, hoping he wouldn't jump over and attack us. The danger was real. Lucky had recently attacked Norbert's sister. She had to be hospitalised for treatment of her injuries. It seemed absurd that after all these months of travel and only weeks away from our home, we were at risk of being attacked by a friend's dog. I also regretted spending so much on food and accommodation, but being too frugal to pay for rabies injections. What had I been thinking?

Just in case my fear of being torn to shreds by Lucky's razor-sharp teeth wasn't enough, we also had to endure his appalling deposits. Lucky was given free reign to toilet at the entrance on the tiled floor. We had to jump over the huge puddles of wee and piles of poo until Hoa, Norbert's cleaner, wiped up the mess. However, on Sunday, Hoa's one day off a week, Han and Norbert, rather than clean up the smelly grotesque mess, would merely scatter a disinfectant powder over it. The sight and stench would saturate the building until Hoa returned the next day.

I later discovered that Hoa was Norbert's ex-mother-in-law. Watching his gorgeous new wife reading fashion magazines on the couch whilst the frail seventy-year-old Hoa scrubbed floors in front of her, made me uncomfortable. It reminded me of the times I didn't treat Nanny with the respect she deserved. At the age of ninety, I used to think her slow-moving, hunched-over walk was an attempt to get attention. If I had been more patient and understanding I would have realised her appearance was due to old age and painful arthritis. Although I cooked her meals, took her to the optometrist and drove her into the countryside on Sundays, stopping for scones and tea, I could have done much more.

I will never forget one winter's morning, a few weeks before Nanny died. Running late for Marco's soccer game, I told her to make her own tea as I rushed out the door. Ordinarily I would make Nanny two cups of hot tea and place them beside her bed, so she could wake up gradually and enjoy cups of tea whilst keeping warm under the covers. However, this cold winter's morning I was running late.

'Sorry Nan, I just don't have time,' I yelled as I slammed the front door and rode off on my bicycle to the game with Marco.

Returning an hour later, my stomach clenched in knots when I saw an ambulance parked in our driveway. Had Nanny died? Had she had another stroke? Should I have left her alone? All these questions rushed through my mind as I sprinted towards the house.

Apparently, Nanny had struggled to lift the milk carton from the fridge and her weak hands had dropped the milk, trying to place it on the bench. Then she lost her balance. Three ribs broke during the fall.

During her second week convalescing in a local rest home she caught pneumonia.

She died three days later.

It would have taken me five minutes to make the tea.

Two years later, I watched Hoa kneeling on the hard wooden floor as she scrubbed. Did I offer to help? Did I tell Han what I was thinking? I didn't say a word. It wasn't my place. I just left the room. Something I regret.

Norbert rang a bell to wake us up for dinner. Jack and I had fallen asleep in the afternoon after our wander around town earlier that morning. Norbert told us to be ready in half an hour. He and Han were taking us for dinner on the other side of town.

I had come to Vietnam wanting to do as the locals did, but the thought of all three of us riding on the backs of Norbert and Han's 50cc scooters freaked me out. The words of Colonel Tran Dao, Traffic Director for the Hanoi Police Department, kept coming back to me, 'The damage caused by traffic accidents stands just behind that caused by the war.' He was referring, only in part, to the 12,000 scooter fatalities Vietnam has each year.

'Here's your helmet,' Norbert said, as he put on his.

'What about the boys?' I asked.

'Children are not legally required to wear helmets, so I don't have any,' Norbert answered.

'What! Are you kidding?'

He wasn't.

'Come on. They'll be fine. Let's go!'

With deep breaths and some reluctance I placed the helmetless Jack behind Norbert and jumped on behind Jack. As Norbert sped off on his red scooter, I held Jack with my left hand and grabbed Norbert's shirt as tightly as possible with my right. Helmetless Marco rode with Han on her blue scooter, his hands gripping the carrier behind him.

'Hold onto Han!' I yelled knowing Marco was too embarrassed to move any closer to her than absolutely necessary.

The idea of going for a scooter ride in Ho Chi Minh was a mother's worse nightmare. The streets were jammed with thousands of scooters, ten abreast, travelling full speed in all directions. The noise of engines revving and horns blaring was deafening. As well as holding my breath to avoid the exhaust fumes, I spent at least half of the twenty-minute journey with my eyes shut, clutching on to Jack and Norbert so tightly that my fingers were stiff when we stopped. So what if scooters were a more environmentally responsible and affordable means of transport! We almost died fifty times, each time saved by mere centimetres.

When Norbert later told me his local hospital sees twelve scooter-related brain injuries each day, I felt nauseous knowing I had allowed my boys to ride without any head protection. However, this experience was soon forgotten as we arrived at our destination, Lang Nuong nam Bo, and smelled the charred aroma of its coal barbeque.

Once seated, I let Norbert do the ordering. It wasn't long before a mini barbeque full of red-hot coals was brought to our table so we could cook our own food. I watched as Norbert and Han placed chunks of meat onto the barbeque. The smell of it made my mouth water, until Han asked, 'Would you like frog, weasel or porcupine?' I replied, 'I think I'll pass.' Had we risked our lives for that?

The sight of skinny frogs legs and porcupine flesh cooking on the barbeque made my stomach tighten and the smell of the charred meat now made me queasy.

'Please Mum, can we go to McDonald's?' Marco whispered. I shook my head, hoping Norbert and Han hadn't heard. The three of us were about to settle for bowls of white rice when the waiter produced fresh plates of raw goat and wild boar. It might not have been chicken or pork, but I was able to convince the boys it would taste just like our barbeques back home. It tasted better.

After Marco cautiously tasted his first piece of goat he wolfed down four skewers worth in record time. When his plate was empty he asked for more. Norbert laughed and said, 'Sure, another plate of goat tits coming up.' Marco was not impressed. To this day, he doesn't seem to mind that I neglected my maternal duties by letting him ride on a scooter without a helmet, risking his life. What he still hates me for is the fact that I didn't protect him from eating goat tits.

After paying a mere twenty-five dollars for the entire bill, we jumped back on the scooters. Riding home, I didn't open my eyes until I felt the scooter come to stop twenty minutes later back at Norbert's. Next day I raced out and bought helmets for Marco and Jack.

As I mentioned earlier, back home in Devonport I felt the boys and I lived in a little bubble of white middle-class safety. Although I loved Devonport's beautiful child-friendly environment, I wanted the boys to know that the world is made up of much more than Gameboys, award-winning cafes, school fairs and people frolicking on the beach.

I wasn't sure they would be old enough to fully understand that we were so close to where war had actually happened, but I wanted Marco to learn about the reality of the Vietnam War rather than playing *Battlefield Vietnam* for hours on my computer, as he did back home.

The boys and I were horrified looking at three jars of preserved human fetuses, deformed by exposure to Agent Orange during the war. Marco, Jack and I spent four hours walking from exhibit to exhibit in the War Remnants Museum. We read personal accounts of the Vietnamese and Americans involved in the war, personal reflections famous for their honest descriptions about the brutal horror of war.

Halfway around the museum Marco asked, 'Didn't the American soldiers deserve what happened to them because they decided to go there?' At the age of ten he thought he knew so much about something so complicated. Obviously, he barely understood.

'Some people fought because they had been raised to believe that their way of life was under threat from these other people,' I said. 'And some did it reluctantly because they had been drafted. And some, Marco, were not much older than you.'

The museum's explicit photographs of the mangled bodies of young American and Vietnamese soldiers and civilians, some the same age as Marco, made him begin to understand that war was not so simple. It was tragic for everyone.

As we walked out the museum gate, Marco and Jack pointed to an elderly beggar on the other side of the street, who with his twisted and limbless body was struggling to move.

'Don't point,' I ordered.

'But that man looks like the men in the photos,' Marco whispered.

I wanted to protect the boys from this distressing sight, but I knew I shouldn't.

Back at Norbert's, I told Marco to ask him about the elderly man. Marco asked Norbert for an orange and said, 'There was a man near the museum who had no legs, but he didn't have a wheelchair like my Uncle Francois. What happened to his legs?'

'He was probably one of many beggars in Ho Chi Minh who are contaminated by Agent Orange which was dropped in areas like Cu Chi during the war,' Norbert said quite casually. 'In fact, the

Vietnamese Government estimates 500,000 children have been born with birth defects caused by contamination with Agent Orange and many of these children are in homes, abandoned by their parents.'

I looked at Marco. His head was lowered and he had stopped peeling his orange. Instead of looking at dinosaur bones, as he had in London's Museum of Natural History, or eating at gourmet restaurants as he had most days in Paris, in Ho Chi Minh he wandered the streets seeing the aftermath of a war. This was a valuable lesson for a young boy like Marco, whose only concept of war was predominantly through glamourized images on a television or a computer screen from the safety of his bedroom or lounge. That was no match for the shock of a ten-year-old witnessing the elderly beggar outside the War Remnants Museum. When Jack put some Vietnam dong in the beggar's empty plastic container, he attempted to cross the street, dragging his legless body on the hard asphalt road whilst dodging hundreds of scooters carelessly flying past.

Later, when Marco said, 'Mum, didn't we eat raw vegetables on our tour to the Cu Chi Tunnels two days ago?' I questioned whether I should have brought the boys to such a risky place. Had we been eating contaminated food? Was I an irresponsible parent? Would Marco be haunted by a world where the images of innocent people affected by war were unbearable to look at? Everyone has their own opinion when it comes to raising children. I can only hope that going to Vietnam was the right choice for Marco and Jack. Perhaps he will begin to question the persecution of minorities, instead of thinking war is just a cool game where 'goodies' kill 'baddies'.

Regardless of the lessons acquired in Ho Chi Minh, it wasn't easy spending four weeks with two young boys alongside cockroaches, dog pee, hot dusty streets, seven million people, over three million life-threatening scooters and the constant fear of rabies. I realised that New Zealand was an idyllic place to live and maybe safety was important too, especially from a mother's point of view?

PART 11
Canada

Chapter 19

Once more at Montreal-Trudeau Airport, Marco, Jack and I threw ourselves into the arms of Marco's *Grandmaman* Simone, Auntie Dan and Uncle Francois. Once again they greeted us with beaming smiles and a box of forty-five soft warm Dunkin' Donuts. Marco dived straight into the pastries and Jack immediately jumped onto Francois' lap seated on his wheelchair.

'Take me for a fast ride!' he cried.

I felt tremendous relief. Finally, I could step back and let someone else take over. We were ushered to Francois' eight-seater van and settled into the back seat. Leaning my head against the window I felt the warm summer's sun on the side of my face and took a deep breath. Aah, back to the familiar. It was a pleasant change to move freely along Montreal's motorway heading to Simone's in comparison with the chaotic roads of Ho Chi Minh. Here I could keep my eyes open without flinching.

As we exited the airport Auntie Dan asked, 'Do you mind if we stop at Costco on the way home to pick up some supplies?'

'Yes, yes, yes!' yelled Marco and Jack, who after months away from shopping malls, longed to buy toys and candy in the gigantic warehouse they had visited seven times during our winter visit. As we trawled the aisles, I wondered how many years of supply Simone was shopping for as she loaded her trolley with a 2.2 kilo box of chocolate brownie mix, a 4.5 kilo bag of pancake mix, a 4 litre jar of mayonnaise and a 16 litre can of canola oil. It was hard not to be tempted to fill a trolley too as we walked through the store. Thank goodness I had a weight limit on my baggage for the flight back to New Zealand.

After three hours shopping in Costco, Dan dropped us off in the quiet suburb of Repentigny outside Simone's house.

I waved as she drove off and then Marco and I made seven trips each from the car to the house to unload Simone's twenty-two bags of groceries. The blanket of snow outside the front door we had left five months ago was now a carpet of bright green grass, lined with rows of blue and purple hydrangeas, basking in Montreal's hot summer sun.

After being imprisoned for countless hours on planes and then another three inside Costco, I suggested we eat dinner in the backyard to make the most of the warm summer evening. When Simone departed for Mass I washed the dishes and tucked the boys into bed. Once they had settled down and read a pile of Tintin books I relaxed in the bath for an hour. When the boys were asleep I put on my pajamas and watched television reruns alone in the lounge. I found myself falling asleep on the couch and finally climbed into the spare room's double bed with Jack, placing a pillow between us to stop him kicking me in the ribs. I stretched out on the freshly laundered sheets of the bed in my cool air-conditioned room and smiled at the thought of Montreal's clean and quiet streets, polite drivers, modern appliances, supermarkets bulging with food and not a cockroach in sight; but, when I tried to sleep I couldn't. Instead my mind replayed and replayed our first day back in Canada from our great European and Asian travels:
- Shopped at Costco
- Cooked dinner
- Ate dinner at six
- Washed dinner dishes
- Jack in bed at seven

- Marco in bed at eight
- Soaked in a bubble bath (alone)
- Watched *Survivor* on the television until I fell asleep on the couch (alone).

I knew the next evening and the next evening and the next evening would be the same until we left one month later. How had it all transformed so quickly from life-and-death adventures to repetitive routines? Drifting off to sleep I wondered whether Vietnam had just been a dream. If I hadn't woken to the sight of Marco counting the 250 packets of Wrigley's gum that he had bought at a local store in Ho Chi Minh to sell to his classmates back in New Zealand for twice the price I might have wondered if I had actually been there.

Although there was certainly a sense of ease and comfort being back with the Rodrigues' the routines all felt so familiar, just as my life back home had been. I began to wonder how I was going to cope living my old life again – a life of order and schedule in a quiet seaside village?

Now it was all over, I yearned for the noise of people laughing and chatting early in the morning in Paris as I went to buy coffee and croissants. The smell of *paella* and pizza at midnight, and the memory of people strolling along the streets in Barcelona and Rome late into the night filled me with longing. Even the memory of Vietnam, with its insects, vermin and hot dusty streets seemed appealing, now I was back in a safe suburban environment. Instead of spontaneously buying meat cooked on hot coals in the street like Ho Chi Minh, meals in Canada were planned a week in advance with food purchased from gigantic, harshly-lit, sterile supermarkets each week. Just like home.

Although Europe had been more predictable than Vietnam, we still lived day to day, buying fresh food at the local market for our evening meal. Alternatively, we would eat out at a restaurant with the locals, so we felt part of the community. In contrast, Repentigny did not promote the mingling of locals on the streets. The roads were too big, the paved sidewalks too few and hardly anybody walked anywhere.

Europeans walked to the supermarket, lingering to chat to the proprietor whom they had known for years. They crammed their brightly-coloured trolleys to the brim with fresh vegetables, fruit and meat. On the way home they stopped to natter to neighbours they met along the way, while licking gelatos they bought from street vendors.

In Repentigny, Simone did no such thing. Instead she sat for hours scrutinizing coupons from three different supermarkets which were mailed weekly. When Jack came in from the garden and pulled on her sleeve wanting her to play cards, Simone didn't budge. She was determined to remain at the table until all the bargains for the week had been identified.

'Mum, I thought we were going to the Botanical Gardens today?' Marco whispered, noticing the coupons spread out over the table.

'It will be too late now,' I replied, trying not to let my own disappointment show.

Finally, when all the circulars had been dissected thoroughly Simone told Marco, Jack and me to hop into her eight-seater van. Once buckled in, we were compelled to join her military-style shop up, visiting Repentigny's Super C, IGA and Loblaws to purchase the bargains and once again, returning home almost three hours later.

Fortunately, I had my first date with Luc to look forward to and prepare for. Luc lived in Vieux Quebec, so, after a second bad night's sleep at Simone's house worrying about returning to everyday routines, I rang Vy at Au Petit Hotel, where we had stayed the previous winter and asked if she had accommodation for a week. I was thrilled when she said she would make room for us. We had only just arrived in Canada two days earlier, but I was determined to fit in one last adventure and this time it would be all mine – a romance.

The timing of our visit to Quebec coincided with the annual Festival D'Été. Six months had passed since we were there for the Festival d'Hiver with its sleighs and a foot of snow. This time it was certainly much easier transporting two kids around the town. For seven days we walked without the difficulty of blizzards and two feet of snow, clad in shorts and t-shirts enjoying the summer temperatures. Around each corner we found live music, somersaulting street entertainers and theatrical characters dressed in bright-coloured clothing.

At every turn I couldn't help wondering whether I might see Luc somewhere tucked in among the hordes of people on the streets. I constantly scanned hundreds of tourists looking for his face in the crowd. I had just one photo of him sent by email wearing a head-to-toe ski outfit, so it would be difficult to pick him out in a group of strangers. Still, I had to be prepared just in case. I wanted him to see me at my best and not when I was in my 'mother' mode, exhausted and disheveled after running behind two energetic children. I wanted him to see the woman who conversed freely, the woman who moved with grace and the woman who wore flowers in her hair. So I panicked when I read the email he sent just after I arrived at Vy's.

I know that finding someone for your children can be a problem and I don't want you to have difficulties or complication with this. If you prefer staying near your boys I can understand. I could go at your hotel like you propose me and just discuss around a cup of coffee or around a picnic during lunch with children around. Let me know what you would prefer.

What!? Did he really think I'd want the boys with me on our first date – interrupting our conversation, wanting to go to the toilet, screaming to go to McDonald's, or wanting to perform arm-farting competitions with Luc? Maybe Luc thought of our date as a casual catch up, but for me it was far more important. I was sure he was the man of my dreams. There would be no kids on our date – of that I was certain.

Though my email exchange with Luc had slowed down during the last month, when I arrived in Canada the communication increased as our meeting drew closer. Luc's words, 'I dream to see you' made me feel his desire to meet me had intensified, especially when he later asked to swap the original plan for a dinner date. He had booked a table at the fine dining restaurant Champlain in the magnificent Château Frontenac. When I told Vy she looked impressed.

'Oh lucky you,' she said. 'That's where Paul McCartney ate when he came to town. It's so posh.'

Wanting to be fully prepared for the evening I checked out the restaurant's website. The description read, 'the intimate dining room serves French and Continental cuisine in a setting adorned with elegant and plush furnishings overlooking the St Lawrence River.' It sounded perfect.

I had spent the days leading up to our first rendezvous picturing how I would feel when Luc and I set eyes on each other again. Would he feel anything for me? Would he find me attractive? Was I going to fancy him, or were my feelings for him a figment of my imagination, like they had been so many times in my past with previous suitors? Did I really want to fall in love? What would happen then? Would he expect me to move to Canada? What about the boys? Would Marco mind changing schools?

I knew before any of these things could actually happen, I needed to prepare for our date. So Marco, Jack and I went shopping. We spent three hours in La Maison Simons department store rushing between lingerie and women's clothing, until Marco and Jack complained they couldn't endure another fashion show squeezed into the claustrophobic, overheated changing room. Finally, after trying on twenty-three outfits, I settled for a silk floral dress and red stilettos, hoping Luc would be swept away by my appearance. I aimed to look perfect, but I still needed a new bra and knickers. I made a deal with the boys if they let me find some new underwear I would take them to visit Parc Valcartier the next day. I had taken the boys there in the winter to slide in tyres on the park's snowy hills. In the summertime, the same site was transformed into a water park. They instantly agreed to the deal, which bought me a few more hours.

The next morning Marco woke early, pulling at my sheets.

'Come on, Mum, get up! You promised to take us to the water park if we let you buy new knickers. Get up!'

When Vy delivered our breakfast tray that morning, she mentioned that each summer Coca-Cola provided a free shuttle bus from the town's centre to the water park. I just needed to purchase a Coke prior to boarding which the driver would take in place of a ticket. Even though the bus tickets only cost a few dollars, I jumped at the chance of a free ride.

After walking the boys down the very steep hill from our hotel to the train station I discovered I had left my purse back in our room. However, I could not face pushing Jack in his pushchair back up the steep hill as I was already sweltering, so since the bus was leaving shortly, I reluctantly left the boys in the station alone.

'Watch Jack like a hawk! And watch yourself, too!' I ordered Marco.

I sprinted up and back down the hill as fast as I could, praying the boys would still be waiting when I returned. Thank God they were.

Out of breath and dripping with sweat, I grabbed them and the pushchair and raced to get on the bus which had just arrived at the depot. I handed the driver my can of Coke that Vy had given me just before we left the hotel.

'Sorry Ma'am, I can't accept a can,' declared the driver. 'It has to be a plastic bottle.'

I looked around and noticed a queue of people behind us, waiting to board the bus.

'Are you kidding?'

He shook his head. No smile.

Maybe I should have just paid for a bus ticket, but there was no way I was going to give up now.

'Can you wait for me?' I asked the driver.

He shrugged his shoulders and reluctantly nodded.

I left the boys on the bus and ran inside the station searching frantically for a store. I spotted a shop on the far side of the building and begged the people lined up at the cashier to let me jump the queue.

I jumped on the bus for the second time, relieved to see the boys still sitting in the back seat and handed the driver the bottle.

The driver shook his head and grunted, 'One bottle per person!'

The entire bus murmured in frustration.

Was I on an episode of *Candid Camera*? No way was I surrendering now.

I ran, queue jumped again, ignored the hissing sounds of other customers and bought two more bottles of Coke.

Nobody enjoyed plunging into the pool more than I did when we arrived at the water park.

Eight hours later, exhausted after our marathon day we struggled up the almost vertical hill from the lower town of Quebec to our hotel. I was sticky and disheveled in the humid summer sun. My hair was still wet from the pool and smelt of chlorine. I couldn't wait to shower and then flop onto the bed and watch a few hours of mindless television. Tomorrow I would make myself gorgeous for Luc. I had my hair appointment at nine a.m. and I was booked in for a pedicure at midday. Thankfully today what I looked like didn't matter.

Suddenly, Marco tugged on my sleeve.

'Mum, who's that man watching us?'

I looked in the direction Marco pointed and froze. There was a man in a dark suit on the other side of the road staring at me. He looked slightly familiar.

It was Luc. Oh God!

No, no, no! I had huge patches of sweat under my arms and across my t-shirt and my hair was plastered to my face by the large straw hat I had been wearing. I quickly removed it and ran my fingers through my hair and then kept my arms down flat tight against my sides.

My knees buckled as Luc crossed the street and approached me. I kept my fingers crossed, hoping Jack would not start a tantrum, demanding the ice cream I had promised him once we returned to our hotel. I had no lollipops on hand this time to keep him quiet. What could I give him? No time to do anything. Luc was almost here.

Breathe.

Breathe.

Just breathe.

Luc smiled as he gave me the traditional *Québécois* kiss on both cheeks. He placed his arms around me. Mine stayed stiff, planted hard against my sides. His reassuring blue eyes stared deeply into mine.

'*Bonjour*, Rebekah,' Luc said as he looked down at my bare legs. I looked down too, aware they badly needed waxing.

'Hi Luc,' I answered, trying to draw his eyes back to my face. 'What a surprise.'

'I hope you don't mind,' he replied. 'My office is nearby and I felt compelled to walk past your hotel during my coffee break in the hope that I might see you.'

I smiled and tried to brush away a piece of hair that was still sticking to my sweaty face.

'Oh, of course not,' I replied, trying not to reveal my state of panic. 'It's great to finally see you.' I flashed him my best and brightest smile.

Great? It was anything but great. It was extremely frustrating. All right for him, I thought – he had the chance to psych himself up for such a meeting. He could comb his hair, wipe his lunch from his face, and stroll over at a leisurely pace. Yet, how could I be angry? Luc had stood waiting on the street for me to arrive. Just like in the movies.

Stumbling over my words, still trying to catch my breath from climbing up the hill, I introduced Marco and Jack to Luc. Jack pointed at my chin and laughed, 'Mummy's got ice cream all over her face!'

I was left speechless.

It was a huge relief when Luc confirmed he was still eager to see me the following night for dinner. Later the same evening, he sent me an email. Apparently, after our meeting he returned to his office and told his secretary he did not want to be disturbed for the rest of the day. With his door locked, he spent the next hours reading over our previous emails. Then he wrote this to me:

Dear woman from the train,

I'm looking for my words, for my sentences, it is not easy to write in another language. Am I under shock? Surely under charms?

This morning, at my job, suddenly I had to stop and something inside me told me to go out and go by your hotel. I was sure to see you . . . don't ask me why . . . it is simply like that. So I stopped the meeting and I told my employees I was feeling bad and I needed some air. I was sure to see you exactly on this street, with your 2 lovely boys. I never had such an intuition like this.

I am really sorry to come like this without warning you before. I realised that perhaps it was not what you really wanted.

I wasn't able to work this afternoon after this encounter. So I am very happy that you still want to see me again tomorrow. I want to be sure to have time to speak in a quiet place. Luc.

So often I have been teased for reading too many books and watching too many films where the characters always find love in the end. So what? At least I knew what I wanted from life and when it came along, I would know what to do, I would be ready.

Now it was my turn for love. Finally.

Next evening I waited in the reception of Au Petit Hotel for Luc, who was to pick me up at seven p.m.

In spite of the effects of her ongoing chemotherapy, Vy offered to babysit the boys for the evening.

'This date is important. It's special,' she said to me when I asked her if one of her nieces could babysit.

'No, Vy, you look too tired. Maybe I could ask Stephan? He lives just around the corner.'

'You can't ask your ex-husband!' she declared. 'I will be fine. I'll just sit quietly and read.'

I knew I should refuse her generous offer, considering she'd had a treatment of chemo the day before, but I couldn't help myself. My future was riding on this date.

'Well, in that case,' I began, 'is there any chance you could take them off my hands a few hours earlier, so I can get my body ready for the big event? Work needs to be done!'

I waxed. I plucked. I straightened this. I tinted that. Mauve eye shadow. Blood red lipstick. A little blush. Black mascara. There was no second chance. I squeezed into my new silk floral dress and into my red stilettos.

I was ready.

Or was I?

A man hadn't seen me naked for nearly four years and travelling through six countries hadn't made me any more comfortable about the prospect. Someone should have stopped me from eating so many bowls of creamy tortellini, crispy *pommes frites* and soft, sugary dough-nuts and drinking gallons of cheap pinot gris and sweet Spanish sangria. Why did the rush of remorse always come when it was already too late? Only two days ago while trying on the silk dress Jack asked, 'Are we having a baby?' as he pointed at my stomach.

'No Jack,' I replied, 'Mummy is just fat.'

It wasn't my arms, legs and bottom I was most concerned about, it was my Buddha belly, which was letting me down. Luckily my volup-tuous bust offered a form of compensation.

Even in my forties I never expected to conform to society's expec-tation of what my body should look like. I cringe at the thought of returning to the time in my twenties when I became obsessed with white spots on my legs caused by severe sunburn. I spent hours researching ways in which I could repair my sun-damaged skin that, in my mind, made me look old. I was twenty-nine at the time. I made an appointment with a skin specialist, who assured me he could 'make my skin youthful again' by pouring acid over my legs. Thank goodness two weeks later I found out I was pregnant and since then haven't had a moment to think about my white spots, let alone spend thou-sands of dollars and hours of pain trying to fix them. Thank goodness.

During my twenties I also ran ten kilometres and took two aerobic classes at the gym most days in order to resemble the models portrayed in the movies and magazines. Since I worked as a flight attendant at this time, with rules insisting I remain an unhealthy size eight, it was difficult to ignore the pressure. Just after my twenty-sixth birthday I worked on a flight to Hawaii. When we arrived I stretched out on a lounger by the hotel pool with my friend Carolyn, hoping to get a tan. When I saw her eating chocolate I asked her for a piece.

'It's not chocolate,' she said. 'It's chocolate laxative. My tummy looks so bloated at the moment. I have to do something.'

I looked down at my own stomach. It was certainly no washboard. 'Can I have a piece, too?' I asked.

The chocolate tasted delicious, so we ended up eating four pieces each. That night on our flight home to New Zealand, Carolyn and I spent nine hours sprinting from our drinks trolley to the toilet, taking turns in ever-increasing agony and deserting our passengers mid-sentence as they attempted to give us their drink orders.

During the last couple of years I have thrown away half the wardrobe from my twenties, but I would rather be a comfortable size fourteen (or sixteen) and enjoy myself, than be constantly dieting or taking laxatives to be a size eight. As a friend once said, 'If you are the size of a house, you might as well add a conservatory.' I really believed myself when I agreed with her, but with an important date in the offering I was once more debating the topic.

As a former chef, I loved food. Of course, this mania had to stop. I wanted to eat with unrestrained abandon. I just hoped soft lighting would be on hand if any clothes were shed at the end of the evening.

I took one last glance in the mirror and then looked out the window. It was five minutes before Luc was supposed to arrive and the sky was blackening. What?! Suddenly, after three days of perfect weather, tonight of all nights it had to rain. I had no umbrella. My silky, straightened hair would now end up a frizzy mop and my mascara would run. Just as I was planning the worst-case scenario, I saw Luc walking towards my hotel carrying two umbrellas. Perfect.

We strolled the short distance to Château Frontenac, Luc in a navy blue suit, crisp white shirt and a red tie while I struggled to prevent the heels of my red stilettos getting wedged in between the cobblestones of the street. People stared at us as we passed arm in arm and I was sure they could feel the magic between us and as we entered the Château's Restaurant Champlain, the *maître'd*'s decision to seat us at a quiet table in the far corner indicated that our chemistry was obvious.

A single white candle burned.

Beethoven's Fifth Symphony played softly in the background.

I felt like Cinderella.

Perfect.

I had planned to play the 'elegant lady' role and order a modest plate of food. However, when Luc took the initiative to order us the degustation menu I felt excited about sampling the chef's six signature dishes. As plate after plate was set before me, I eagerly savoured the delicious smoked char, mussel soup, grilled quail, honey and goat's cheese sherbet and veal cutlet with truffles.

Halfway through the meal the waiter noticed Luc had hardly touched his food and asked, 'Was your meal unsatisfactory, *Monsieur?*' Luc stared directly into my eyes and replied, 'I did not come here to eat.' The waiter seemed a little confused. I wasn't. I swallowed the last morsel of veal on my plate, put down my fork and smiled.

Right from the beginning of the evening, I found myself at ease in Luc's company. We talked about our mutual love of travel, our attraction to each other and our childhood dreams. We laughed. I touched his arm. He stroked my hand. We stared longingly into each other's eyes – then the waiter brought my favourite dessert – *crème brûlée*. Nothing could be more perfect.

Then it happened. Luc took my hand and looked deeply into my eyes. I batted my eyelashes a few times and then closed my eyelids waiting for a kiss.

'Rebekah,' Luc whispered.

'Yes?' I replied waiting for his embrace.

'I'm married.'

It took me a few stunned seconds to understand. Married? What had he just said? Married?

I wished Beethoven would bloody shut up.

To this day, I consider it one of my proudest achievements that even in that moment, after his declaration, I didn't pause. I never missed a beat.

'Why in that case are you sitting here with me?' I snapped, yanking my hand away from his.

'I felt totally compelled to meet you,' came his reply.

What? For over four months I had been getting to know this man intimately. We had both written stories about our past. We had talked about our own dreams for the future. All the while I had stupidly assumed maybe he could be the one. I had hoped that finally I might stroll hand in hand with a lover along the beach on a Sunday afternoon, like I had seen so many couples do while I spent Sunday after Sunday alone with my boys. What made it even more difficult was I actually liked Luc. He had seemed such a gentleman. Then again, why had I expected this guy to be the one? My track record has certainly never been impressive when it came to picking a soul mate.

With my head in my hands, my stunned shock was broken by the crash of cutlery to the floor. Luc looked down and bit his lip.

After picking up my knife and fork he murmured, 'I'm incredibly attracted to you, Rebekah. I just can't have a relationship with you right now. I can't leave my wife. She's . . .'

'She's what?'

'She's pregnant.'

Bloody perfect!

Just then he pulled out his guitar, which he had brought to the restaurant. He wanted to know if I would let him sing *Woman on a Train* before we parted?

'No!' I said. 'Absolutely not!

I'd had enough.

'I feel certain we will meet again,' he sweetly declared, without showing any sign of remorse or rejection. 'And I will never forget this evening with you. I love it when you smile, when you dive into my eyes, when you eat when I don't.'

I almost chocked on my after-dinner mint.

I stood up and beckoned for the waiter.

'Bring me a doggie bag,' I demanded.

The waiter was about to protest, '*Madame*, we don't . . .' but when he saw my red face, scuttled off immediately and handed me a piece of tin foil.

I grabbed Luc's umbrella, picked up his untouched dessert and stormed out of the restaurant. I shoved the umbrella into the nearest rubbish bin and let the pounding rain wash over me as I began the journey to the hotel.

Chapter 20

Adventures over. Hopes of romance, dead. We were returning home and I couldn't think of a single thing to look forward to. For nearly eight months my mind had been free of domestic clutter: phone calls, housework, bills and chores. Marco understood the importance of this. When I asked him, 'What are you going to miss most about our trip?' he answered, 'Freedom.'

'If we did it once Marco, there's no reason why we couldn't do it again,' I said, trying to be optimistic.

Marco lowered his head, knowing that right now he was heading back to the four walls of a classroom with a strict schedule and set of rules, not to mention the boring cheese sandwich, apple and banana that filled his lunchbox five days a week.

I was also anxious about the immediate future. I needed employment. I had to buy a car and there was the question of whether we should stay in our two-bedroom apartment, which was more like a motel unit than a home. Another prospect loomed as well, that of continuing my future alone.

Of course not everything about our trip had been smooth sailing. Marco, Jack and I were beginning to argue, not surprising considering we had spent so much time so close to each other, often sleeping and living in the confines of one small room. Consequently the idea of the boys back at school and crèche for part of the day was not unwelcome. At last, I would have a little time to myself when I could remove the hairs from my legs without Jack knocking my pot of hot wax over the carpet or bleach my moustache without Marco collapsing in fits of laughter. The greatest relief would be not worrying about the boys' noise, especially in hotels with paper-thin walls. Recently while staying at Au Petit Hotel, we were recovering from jet lag after returning to Montreal from Vietnam. Jack woke at three in the morning and started shouting, 'I want a cup of tea' (his toddler language for hot milk). I had no milk. This meant I would have to venture out into the night and search for a shop that was open, buy a carton of milk, then return to the hotel and heat it up in the communal microwave. I flatly refused and tried to ignore him, but his incessant loud wailing, 'I want a cup of tea' increased. I turned over and threw the blankets over my head, but after his thirty-fourth request a voice from the room next door roared, 'Give him a bloody cup of tea!'

I leapt out of bed, threw on a tracksuit, made sure the door was locked and headed outside to find some 'bloody' milk.

In spite of all the difficult moments which had arisen on our travels as I sat at the table with *Grandmaman* Simone having our last meal in Canada, I felt a sudden heaviness in my chest. Would we still eat meals together as a family, sitting at a table, laughing, talking and playing card games when we arrived home each night? Or would Jack end up eating cold leftover lasagna in the car as I drove Marco to basketball practise, the way it had been before we left? Would the often tedious, monotonous and thankless tasks associated with parenting cause me to be short-tempered and scream at the boys, 'I've had enough of you two!' while simultaneously knocking back a large glass of Chardonnay, before dinner, a.k.a. witching hour?

While watching Marco and Jack, now dealing cards for a game of 500, the realisation dawned that I had been searching for something which had always been in front me. It was my boys, my very own family who, despite all the trouble they caused, had given me the most pleasure during our trip.

Certainly new and exotic places had helped to satisfy my need for adventure, but I also received so much joy from spending quality time with Marco and Jack without the pressure of routines. I hoped I could find extra strength not to revert to my old ways. That busy life often led me to fatigue, leaving me no energy to play with my kids, let alone care for them properly. Like the time I came home late from a staff meeting at school just after we had moved into our new apartment. Jack wanted to clean his teeth but most of our toiletries were still packed in boxes stored in the garage one floor below our apartment. Too tired to go looking I discovered an old airline pack of toothpaste in the bathroom, which I promptly used to clean Jack's teeth. When Marco later asked me for the toothpaste I told him to use the same tube I had left in the bathroom.

'Is it the one that says Old Spice?' Marco shouted.

Shame on me! I had cleaned my two-year-old's teeth with shaving cream.

'Boys! Stop fighting! You're annoying that lady.'

I saw the scowls as we lined up to board the plane. Occasionally a passenger looked sympathetic, but mostly, there were looks of disdain.

After fastening our seatbelts I tried to block out their noise with my iPod. It seemed forever before the hostess delivered a much-needed glass of chardonnay. Now I just had to endure the next twenty-odd hours until we landed in New Zealand.

The first two hours from Montreal to Los Angeles were hell. Jack wouldn't settle and twenty minutes after takeoff he had knocked a glass of orange juice over my white pants. One female passenger trying to work on her computer kept looking our way and glaring. I was trying to keep Jack quiet with food, crayons and pink nail polish, but to be realistic he was a normal, lively three-year-old. No one could expect a toddler to remain silent indefinitely and if you travel on public transport can you really expect a quiet environment?

Apparently this leather-clad, butch-looking woman demanded silence. When she could not restrain herself any longer, she turned and shouted, 'Tell him to frigging shut up!'

She had picked on the wrong mother.

'I know it was a long time ago,' I responded, 'but you were a child once too.'

'Yes,' she snapped. 'However, I had parents who knew how to look after me properly!'

Did this woman have any feelings at all? Didn't she know my heart was broken and I felt all adventure in my life was over? Worse still, this was the first leg of our return home and there remained a torturous eighteen hours of travel to endure with a manic toddler.

After much persuasion and bribery Jack finally fell asleep. It was now my turn to switch off, but my mind was wired. I was about to return to my old life. Everything was going to be the same, almost as if I had never left. Could I cope with the same routine I had left eight months ago, drinking coffee alone at the kitchen table trying to read my morning paper alongside the deafening sound of cartoons? A life with no gradual introduction to the new day – just the ceaseless demands of two young boys needing clothes, breakfast, lunch boxes and much more. As for the evenings alone, the television is my partner and the only recipient of my touch, the remote control. Could I handle going back to the same single bed alone? My story was no *Eat Pray Love*. It was more like *Eat, Watch 'The Bachelor,' Sleep*.

Then it happened.

Row thirty-six.

Aisle seat.

Shoulder length hair – greying a little.

He turned briefly and caught my eye.

I detected a smile.

A kind face.

Green eyes.

Sun-bronzed skin.

Reaching into his leather satchel he placed a small book of poetry on his tray – Leonard Cohen's *The Book of Longing*. Perfect!

'Stay there Marco and keep an eye on your brother! I need to go and freshen up.'

Gratitude

My deepest thanks goes to the following individuals.

My sons Marco and Jack, who didn't bat an eyelid when I told them we were selling the house and going on an eight-month adventure around the world. Even greater gratitude is necessary for their allowing me to return home and write about them – not that they had a choice! To my grandmother Nanny, who gave me the inspiration to follow my dream, a woman who taught me to work hard and keep smiling regardless of the hardships in life. To my mother Alison, who made the brave decision to give birth to me when she was nineteen and single, knowing that having a child could put stress on her already fragile heart and shorten her life.

To my straight-talking editor Kineret Yardena, who spent two years helping me transform *Full Tilt* from a first draft to the book it is today by introducing me to the writer's toolbox and later forming my writers' group. To Kineret, Deirdre Thurston and Gen Lynch, my fellow writers' group members, who kept me on track with monthly deadlines, offered me their diverse opinions about *Full Tilt* and gave me a safe place to cry when I felt overwhelmed by the juggling of writing, motherhood and life!

To my dear friend Susan Waddell, who painstakingly read through my manuscript, correcting spelling and grammar and attempting to rid *Full Tilt* of the occasional expletive!

To my essential friends who sustained me during the four years it took to write *Full Tilt*. Your help with the book's content, constant encouragement and unconditional care of my boys when I had a deadline to meet was absolutely necessary to the publication of *Full Tilt*; Fiona Ironside, Lucy Smith, Rebecca Woolfall, Parisa Taghizadeh, Gillian Twiss, Julie Soboil, Sarah Walker, Susan Welch, Cathy Chambers, Dinah Saxby, Cathy Fraser, Fiona Richardson – I thank you all.

To editors Geoff Walker and Arnie Weismann, who gave me their valuable feedback, and an agent who turned me down upon receiving my first draft! The agent's words, 'I don't care about the character Rebekah, because I know nothing about Rebekah', prompted me to spend the next four years scratching the surface and rewriting *Full Tilt* to reveal what Geoff Walker described as 'deprecating self honesty'. To Joan Rosier-Jones, for motivating my writing with her Nuts & Bolts of Writing course at the University of Auckland.

To my publishers, Mary Egan, Sophia Egan-Reid and Anna Egan-Reid, who spent hours working back and forth with my ever-changing ideas about *Full Tilt*'s layout and cover. To my wonderful friend and illustrator Nina Rycroft, who patiently worked with me during this creative process – I love my *Full Tilt* cover!

To all the generous folk I met during our world trip, without whom many of the stories in *Full Tilt* would never have existed: the Rodrigue Family in Montreal, VY in Old Quebec, Luc on the train between Montreal and Quebec, my family in England, Christine Smith on the Isle of Wight, Luca and Julia Bevilaqua in London, Isabella Delneufcourt in Paris, Ian and Marielise Logan in Villefranche, Nicolas De Leon, Christophe, Freya and Chloe in Alet les Bains, Cecelia and Oscar Torrent in Barcelona, Jill, Prisca and Michele Bevilaqua in Rome, and Norbert and Han Ehrbar in Ho Chi Minh – you are all welcome at my home in New Zealand anytime!